GEOLOGY

 CLIMATE

 OCEANOGRAPHY

 NEARSHORE

 PLANTS

 ANIMALS

 HUMAN IMPACT

 MONITORING

UNDERSTANDING THE LIFE OF
Point Loma

Cabrillo National Monument Foundation
San Diego, California

Cabrillo National Monument Foundation

1800 Cabrillo Memorial Drive
San Diego, California 92106

Library of Congress Cataloging-in-Publication Data
Understanding the Life of Point Loma.
    p. cm.
    Includes bibliographical references.
    ISBN 0-941032-08-6 (alk. paper)
    1. Natural history—California—Loma, Point. 2. Coastal ecology—California—Loma, Point. I. Cabrillo National Monument Foundation.

    QH105.C2U54 2004
    508.794'98—dc22

                                    2004054481

First Edition 2004
Designed and produced by Christina Watkins and Amanda Summers, Prescott, AZ
Edited by Rose Houk, Flagstaff, AZ
CNMF Project Editor: James D. Nauman
CNMF Project Coordinator: Karen Eccles
Printed in the U.S.A.

ABOUT CABRILLO NATIONAL MONUMENT FOUNDATION

Cabrillo National Monument Foundation is a nonprofit organization dedicated, in cooperation with the National Park Service, to the support of preservation and enhancement of the natural, cultural, historical, scientific, and educational resources of Cabrillo National Monument. Chartered in 1956, the Foundation is governed by a volunteer board of directors.

If you are interested in becoming a member of CNMF, please contact us at:
    Cabrillo National Monument Foundation
    1800 Cabrillo Memorial Drive
    San Diego, California, 92106
    619-222-4747
    www.cnmf.org

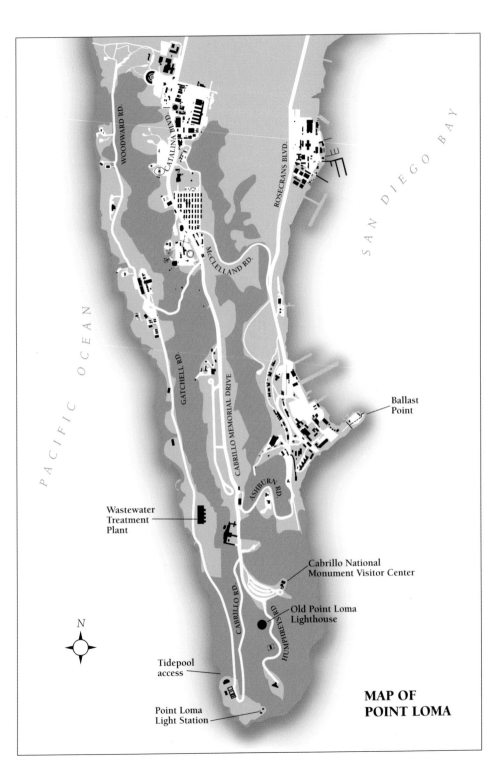

PACIFIC OCEAN

SAN DIEGO BAY

WOODWARD RD.

CATALINA BLVD.

ROSECRANS BLVD.

McCLELLAND RD.

GATCHELL RD.

CABRILLO MEMORIAL DRIVE

ASHBURN RD.

Ballast
Point

Wastewater
Treatment
Plant

Cabrillo National
Monument Visitor Center

Old Point Loma
Lighthouse

CABRILLO RD.

HUMPHREYS RD.

Tidepool
access

Point Loma
Light Station

N

**MAP OF
POINT LOMA**

CONTENTS

Introduction **8**
Terry DiMattio, Superintendent, Cabrillo National Monument

CHAPTER ONE • From Sea to Shore: Geologic History *12*
Patrick Abbott, PhD, and Thomas K. Rockwell, PhD

CHAPTER TWO • The Highs and the Lows: Climate & Oceanography *30*
Reinhard E. Flick, PhD

CHAPTER THREE • Tidepools & Kelp Forests: Nearshore Environments *54*
Bonnie J. Becker, MA, Mia Tegner, PhD, Paul Dayton, PhD

CHAPTER FOUR • A Mediterranean Place: Plant Communities *84*
Kathryn McEachern, PhD

CHAPTER FIVE • Life on the "Island": Animals **112**
Robert Fisher, PhD

CHAPTER SIX • People on Point Loma: History of Human Impacts *132*
Samantha Weber, MA

CHAPTER SEVEN • Taking the Vital Signs: Monitoring & Management *158*
Samantha Weber, MA

Index **175**

Photography and Illustration Credits **184**

You are holding in your hands a unique book. It is the first book ever written about the natural resources of Point Loma, both those found on the peninsula and those from the kelp forest offshore to the tidepools, where the ocean meets the land. Why a book on these resources? Simply put, these remaining marine and terrestrial resources are in jeopardy. As southern California has grown, the biologically diverse habitat that covers the hills and canyons, and the vulnerable tidepools along the shore, have become increasingly rare and important. What was once common is now scarce and should be preserved for the education and enjoyment of future generations.

AUTHOR

Terry DiMattio is superintendent of Cabrillo National Monument. He has been associated with Cabrillo National Monument since 1972 when he started as a volunteer.

If we are to successfully preserve these precious natural resources, three things should happen. First, the agencies, the stewards that have been entrusted with their care, need to learn more about the plants and animals that live here, how many there are, what kind of condition they are in, and if their health is improving, holding steady, or declining. Second, we need to identify and remove the exotic, or nonnative, plants and animals that threaten these natural resources. And third, the people who own this land, the citizens of the United States who visit and cherish places like Cabrillo National Monument, need to learn about these vulnerable resources and understand why they are important. It is only with the understanding and support of the public that we will be able to protect and restore the home of the gray fox, Pacific rattlesnake, Orcutt's spineflower, aggregating anemone, black abalone, and ochre sea star.

Point Loma has often been described as an island, though in fact it is connected to the mainland. Still, the natural resources on the peninsula have been cut off, isolated from similar habitat by the growth of San Diego. Thankfully, the rocky intertidal and the coastal sage scrub, maritime succulent scrub, southern maritime chaparral, and other types of habitats have been somewhat protected from development by the presence of the federal government. As a result, more than half the open space within the federal reservation on Point Loma is undeveloped. The City of San Diego Wastewater Department, Department of Veterans Affairs, National Park Service, U.S. Coast Guard, and U.S. Navy are preserving this open space in the Point Loma Ecological Reserve, and the National Park Service and the Navy are actively protecting the tidepools on the ocean side of the peninsula.

This book gives an overview of Point Loma's natural resources and what is being done to learn about and preserve them. In the first chapter, Dr. Patrick L. Abbott and Dr. Thomas K. Rockwell, of San Diego State University, provide the foundation. In understandable language, they introduce the geology of Point

Loma and how the peninsula came to be formed over the past 80 million years. Dr. Reinhard E. Flick, Scripps Institution of Oceanography, follows in his chapter with an explanation of San Diego's weather and climate, and the ocean's effect on climate.

National Park Service marine biologist Bonnie Becker, along with Dr. Paul Dayton and the late Dr. Mia Tegner of Scripps Institution of Oceanography, take you on a tour of the world beneath the surface of the sea. Their chapter explores the nearshore environment surrounding the peninsula—the rocky intertidal and the kelp forest to the west. They will take you on a journey through the different zones of each area and introduce the colorful inhabitants.

With the construction of each new suburb and mall, and the highways that connect them, we have lost hundreds of thousands of acres of the Mediterranean plant community that exists in southern California and only four other places in the world. Dr. Kathryn McEachern, a plant ecologist with the U.S. Geological Survey, is intimately familiar with Point Loma's native vegetation. In Chapter 4 she talks about the rare and sensitive plant communities found here and how they have adapted to a short, cool rainy season and the long, dry, warm spring, summer, and fall. Plants with strange-sounding names—lemonadeberry, chamise, snake cholla, fishhook cactus, wart-stemmed ceanothus, live-forever, toyon, and sea dahlia—have all found a home on the windswept terraces and in the sheltered canyons of Point Loma.

Similarly, the reptiles, amphibians, mammals, birds, and insects have adapted to the same temperate climate that has attracted millions of people to southern California. Dr. Robert Fisher, also with the U.S. Geological Survey, has been studying the herpetofauna (reptiles and amphibians) and macroinvertebrates (insects, spiders, bugs, and scorpions) of Point Loma for several years. His chapter is filled with interesting and little-known facts about the animals that struggle for survival among the sage and buckwheat.

Point Loma is home not only to plants and animals. Humans have a long, rich history here as well. Samantha Weber, former Chief of Natural Resource Science at Cabrillo National Monument, recounts the story of humans on the peninsula, from the earliest Native Americans to today's rangers and scientists, and shares the effects we have had on the natural resources here. Throughout this period of human occupation, the landscape has undergone many changes. Now the question is, "What is being done to preserve these rare and sensitive habitats?"

Weber addresses this question in the last chapter of the book, with a look at the programs and activities that the City of San Diego, Department of Veterans Affairs, National Park Service, Coast Guard, and Navy have implemented over the past several years. Scientists, rangers, and concerned volunteers young and old are working diligently to learn about the natural resources here and taking steps to preserve them. They have devoted countless early morning hours to trapping herps and collecting data about their abundance and distribution. They have crawled on hands and knees through pungent sage and spiny cactus to lay out transects and count the number and types of plants within them. They have collected and analyzed scat, pulled up prickly yellow star thistle and *Carpobrotus* sp., and chopped down thousands of nonnative acacia trees. They have waded in cold seawater in search of once plentiful abalone. And they have read and studied and prepared talks about the intriguing and precious plants and animals of Point Loma. They have done all this so that we, and those who follow us, will be able to learn about and explore this place called Point Loma.

I hope you enjoy this unique book, and that after you have read it you will see Point Loma and its natural resources in a new light, and will want to join in the efforts to preserve and restore them.

From Sea to Shore: Geologic History

The geologic history of Point Loma is a story dominated by two periods of time—when the rocks formed, and when they were uplifted and shaped into the peninsula we see today. First, the peninsula's main mass of rocks accumulated as sand, mud, and gravel dumped into the Pacific Ocean during the late Cretaceous Period, about 76 to 72 million years ago. Then, those sedimentary rocks were uplifted and deformed by faulting, cut across by ancient beaches and sea floors, and modified by erosion during the last 2 million years or so.

AUTHORS

Dr. Patrick L. Abbott is a Professor of Geology at San Diego State University. His research specialty is reading the history stored in sedimentary rocks. He is author of the textbooks, *Natural Disasters*, and *The Rise and Fall of San Diego*.

Dr. Thomas K. Rockwell is a Professor of Geology at San Diego State University. His research specialty is determining the sizes and frequencies of prehistoric earthquakes. He is currently working on faults in the United States, Mexico, Turkey, Israel, Mongolia, and Argentina.

THE CRETACEOUS

If we travel back in time some 80 million years to visit the area that later would become Point Loma, we'd be on a boat floating in the Pacific Ocean in water about 3,500 feet deep. Looking to the east we would see the ancient shoreline, foothills, and ancestral Peninsular Ranges. The mountains and hills were being eroded by seasonal rains and stream floods that delivered sediment (sand, mud, gravel) to the shoreline. As erosion and sedimentation continued, some of the sediment flowed seaward and was deposited in a submarine fan. This submarine fan, put in place 76 to 72 million years ago, is what now makes up most of the elongate mass of eroded sedimentary rocks we know as Point Loma.

A submarine fan is a huge apron of sediment that builds out onto the ocean

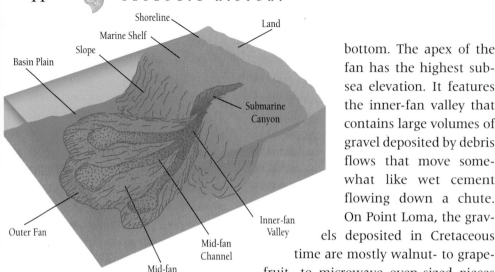

Shoreline

Land

Marine Shelf

Slope

Basin Plain

Submarine Canyon

Outer Fan

Inner-fan Valley

Mid-fan Channel

Mid-fan Interchannel

Submarine fan.

Cretaceous conglomerate and sandstone outcrop along Cabrillo Road, deposited in an inner submarine fan environment.

bottom. The apex of the fan has the highest subsea elevation. It features the inner-fan valley that contains large volumes of gravel deposited by debris flows that move somewhat like wet cement flowing down a chute. On Point Loma, the gravels deposited in Cretaceous time are mostly walnut- to grapefruit- to microwave oven-sized pieces of eroded bedrock now cemented into what is known as a conglomerate. These gravel-sized pieces in the conglomerate originated from the metamorphic, volcanic, and plutonic rock bodies found in the hills and mountains to the east. Good exposures of these inner-fan valley conglomerates can be seen in the cut bank behind the wastewater treatment plant and in the road cuts along Cabrillo Road within the national monument.

The middle part of a submarine fan is marked by sand-filled channels and areas between the channels. Mid-fan channels are wide and have flat bottoms. Sands carried to the shoreline by rivers may accumulate in unstable masses that can overcome inertia and flow downslope, like a moving carpet of quicksand. A few sand-flow and deposition events may fill a channel, causing later sands to flow down new channels that form in lower-elevation portions of the fan. Channels form and fill in a radial pattern that sweeps back and forth across the fan, building the fan up and out. Good places to see the Cretaceous-age, sand-filled, mid-fan channels are at Sunset Cliffs, 4.5 miles north of the monument, and in the road cuts going down the Bayside Trail in the park.

The mid-fan channels were filled by westward-flowing sands, creating a "skeletal" structure. Between the channels are topographic low areas. Some flow events are so large that the flowing water/sediment masses overtop the banks of the mid-fan channels and then flow north or south into the mid-fan interchannel areas where they deposit mud and very fine sand. The fine sediments sort themselves out by size—the coarsest

LEFT: **South of Ladera Street are exposures of mid-fan interchannel, overbank sediments deposited as graded beds, in which suspensions of sediment settled out coarsest grains first, followed by progressively finer sediments.**

pieces settle from suspension first, followed by progressively finer sediments. These fine sediments contain a good deal of organic detritus that gives a gray color to the rocks. This organic material was once a food source for many invertebrates, which left traces of their activities as burrows, grazing and locomotion tracks, and resting indentations. These trace fossils, and the mid-fan interchannel sedimentary rocks, are well exposed and visible in the sea cliffs at the foot of Ladera Street at Sunset Cliffs and in the tidepools in the park.

Over millions of years, some of the sediments brought to the shoreline fed the growing submarine fan. At 80 million years ago, looking down from our imaginary boat floating over the site of today's Point Loma, mud-sized sediment was settling from suspension in seawater and being deposited on the sea floor. During the next several million years, as the submarine fan built westward, the mud layers were buried beneath sand

CENTER: **Gray, organic-rich mudstones contain Cretaceous fossil logs south of Ladera Street.**

RIGHT: **Cretaceous grazing trails of invertebrate animals are well exposed at the tidepool area along the west coast in Cabrillo National Monument.**

sheets and channels. Then, as the submarine fan continued its upward-and-outward growth, the sand units were in turn buried beneath gravel layers.

Then, this millions-of-years-long pattern of sediment being added to the seaward-growing fan abruptly changed style. We see evidence of this in a shift in sediment sizes. The coarsening-upward pattern of mud, overlain by sand, then overlain by gravel was reversed as sand layers were deposited on top of the gravel. What might have interrupted the pattern? One possibility is an interval of faulting, which could have changed the water depth and sedimentation. An example of the evidence of the changed conditions can be seen just after reaching the park's entrance station. In the road cut on the left, the large greenish boulder of Santiago Peak Volcanics rock is surrounded by sandstone. This boulder, and others at the same level, may have fallen directly off a fault scarp (cliff) onto the submarine fan. The mega-boulder horizon marks the change from gravel (conglomerate) beds below to sand (sandstone) beds above. These upper sandstone beds are exposed all the way down the Bayside Trail.

How is it that the sediments deposited two-thirds of a mile deep in the Pacific Ocean are now seen above sea level as Point Loma? How did such a drastic change occur? The answer is a squeezing force—called compression—that occurred on the west side of the Rose Canyon fault system. This caused the Cretaceous sedimentary rocks to be folded into a U-shaped fold (a syncline) that tilts down to the east. If you pushed both sides of a piece of paper into a U shape, then tilted it slightly sideways, you'd get the effect. At the tidepools and on the Bayside Trail, note that the originally horizontal sedimentary rock layers are now inclined 5 degrees to 15 degrees to the northeast. The other side of the syncline is seen in La Jolla and Bird Rock, where the sedimentary rock layers dip 5 degrees to 15 degrees to the southeast. The entire fold then tilts slightly to the east.

The Cretaceous marine sedimentary rocks are only found in San Diego on the west side of the Rose Canyon fault system, where intense compression and faulting have caused uplift. And, movements on the Rose Canyon fault have not stopped.

THE QUATERNARY

The Quaternary, the most recent period of geologic time, includes the last 2.67 million years, from the Pleistocene (Ice Age) through the Holocene (modern or recent) epochs. Much of the Quaternary history of the San Diego region is preserved because there have been no major periods of deformation to cause deep burial, or uplift and removal by erosion. The exceptions are in the downtown and bay areas, where subsidence has allowed burial of most of the Quaternary deposits, and in areas like Mt. Soledad and Point Loma, where localized uplift and erosion have removed some deposits.

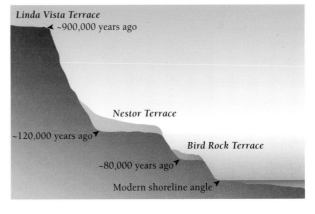

At Point Loma, three basic types of Quaternary deposits are preserved locally: marine terrace alluvium (water deposited), aeolian (windblown) sand, and colluvium (gravity deposited).

MARINE TERRACES Marine terraces are essentially uplifted, abandoned beach lines and sea floors. They are composed of a basal erosion surface caused by wave abrasion (the abrasion platform) and are usually covered with a thin veneer of marine or beach deposits in which fossils are sometimes preserved. The abrasion platform usually slopes gently seaward (or bayward), and is commonly steepest near the ancient beach line. Landward, the back edge of the ancient shoreline of a marine terrace usually can be recognized by the presence of an old, abandoned sea cliff

Schematic cross section showing marine abrasion platforms (old sea floors = terraces) at the top of Point Loma (Linda Vista terrace) down to the modern shoreline.

or area where the ground rises rapidly. At Point Loma, several ancient beaches are preserved as marine terraces and can be viewed in various areas on the peninsula.

The preserved marine terraces at Point Loma vary from about 80,000 to about 900,000 years old. Each marine terrace represents a period when sea level was relatively high

The Bird Rock and Nestor terraces are visible from the tidepools at Point Loma.

and close to the present worldwide sea level. During these several-thousand-year-long periods of high sea level, coastal waves cut a new terrace and a new sea cliff. Then, when climate turned cooler and ice accumulated on the continental areas of the Northern Hemisphere, sea level dropped as evaporated water fell as snow and became locked up in glaciers.

Sea level drops at about the same time around the world. These periods of relatively low sea level may extend for several tens of thousands of years; they correspond to past advances of continental glaciers. During these times, the Pacific coast lay several miles west of the present coastline and all of San Diego and Point Loma were high and dry. During glacial times Point Loma was no more than an inland promontory, rather than a peninsula as it is today.

The lowest two marine terraces on Point Loma date at about 80,000 and 120,000 years in age—the Bird Rock and Nestor terraces, respectively. The dates come from one of the more common solitary corals (*Balanophyllia elegans*) that is sufficiently abundant as a fossil in the Point Loma marine terrace deposits. Corals incorporate uranium into the cellular structure of their skeletons when they are alive, and so they are usually reliable for providing age control of marine terrace deposits; in fact, most dating of terraces and ancient reefs around the world is done on corals. At Point Loma, both the Bird Rock and Nestor terraces have been dated by analyzing the ratios of various types of uranium and thorium (by-products of the radioactive decay of uranium). The dates acquired locally agree well with those collected from other marine terraces in California, as well as those from ancient reef tracts in the tropics. This is but one line of evidence showing that sea levels have varied synchronously around the world, and can be attributed to astronomical variations such as precession of the Earth around the Sun, changes in the eccentricity of Earth's orbit, and variations in Earth's axis of tilt. For the past several hundred thousand years, major worldwide highstands of sea level have had a period of about 100,000 years with intervening periods of glacial advance. The last major period of glaciation reached a maximum ice advance about 20,000 years ago; then the ice began to melt and sea level began to rise. Sea level has been close to its current level for about the past 6,000 years.

The oldest marine terraces at Point Loma occupy the highest topographic positions and correlate to the Linda Vista sequence of terraces in San Diego. Much of the City of San Diego is built on the extensive mesas that comprise this sequence; these terraces are thought to be in the range of 680,000 to 930,000 years in age.

UPLIFT AND FAULTING Marine terraces are useful landforms because they provide information on the absolute uplift or subsidence of coastlines. If we know the age of a terrace and the elevation of sea level at the time the terrace formed, we can determine the amount of uplift of the land. Because worldwide sea level has varied systematically throughout the world, study of coral reefs in the tropics has provided detailed information on the elevation of the oceans at various periods throughout Quaternary time. By dating local terraces, such as the Bird Rock and Nestor terraces, it is possible to correlate them to those in tropical regions where the reef ages and their elevations of formation are known. For Point Loma, the 80,000-year-old Bird Rock terrace was originally formed when sea level was 5 to 10 feet lower than its current level. In contrast, sea level 120,000 years ago, the time of the Nestor terrace, was about 20 feet higher than present (which is what is likely to happen should global warming continue to melt the polar ice caps). Knowing these paleo-sea level elevations and the current heights of about 30 feet for the Bird Rock terrace and 70 feet for the Nestor terrace, we can calculate that Point Loma has been rising slowly, at about 5 inches every thousand years. In contrast, some rapidly uplifting areas of the world are rising at rates as high as 30 feet every thousand years (for example, portions of Ventura, California, and the Himalayan Mountains in Asia). As with Point Loma, most of San Diego County is also rising at about 5 inches per thousand years, with the exception of Mt. Soledad, which is rising a little faster—about 8 inches per thousand years due to

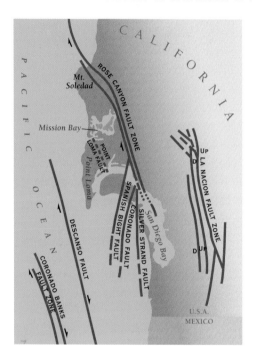

Point Loma is a mass of rock uplifted by fault actions.

activity of the Rose Canyon fault. San Diego Bay, in contrast, is subsiding at a low rate but fast enough to keep the bay area at or below sea level (along with a little erosional help from the area's rivers).

Map of Mercalli intensities (which can range from I to XII) felt during the May 27, 1862, earthquake. Point Loma was near the epicenter of the fault movement, which may have occurred offshore.

Much of coastal San Diego lies astride the active Rose Canyon fault zone. In fact, San Diego owes much of its beauty to this fault, which is responsible for the uplift of Mt. Soledad and the rocky coastline of La Jolla, as well as the subsidence in San Diego and Mission bays. Without the fault, San Diego would not have a harbor and probably would not have been settled as it was. The down side, of course, is that San Diego is occasionally frequented by large earthquakes, perhaps even as large as 7.4 magnitude. The last moderately large local earthquake struck San Diego on May 27, 1862, and measured about 5.9 magnitude. Geologic studies show that the last very large earthquake on the Rose Canyon fault occurred just before San Diego was founded, sometime between the years 1500 and 1769, and produced up to 10 feet of lateral motion at Rose Creek. (For comparison, the 1992 Landers earthquake was 7.4 magnitude and the 1999 Hector Mine earthquake was 7.1 magnitude; both exhibited average displacements of about 10 feet.)

Point Loma is cut by a number of secondary strands of the Rose Canyon fault zone. Most were early players in the complex history and development of the fault zone and are no longer active. Where exposed below marine terraces, most Point Loma faults do not cut the last interglacial terraces (80,000 to 120,000 years old) and are not considered a seismic risk. The Point Loma fault, which runs along the eastern side of the peninsula, has not been sufficiently studied. Although some studies have suggested recent activity for it, landsliding also may have played a role in its expression. More work is warranted to demonstrate if this fault is still active.

At some time in the geologic past, fault activity was responsible for helping shape Point Loma's topography. The same Cretaceous sedimentary rocks that form the bulk of the peninsula lie one mile below the surface at Imperial Beach. Clearly, significant upward and downward movements have occurred along ancient coastal faults. The Point Loma peninsula has been a beneficiary, as these fault movements have left it standing high and beautiful.

AEOLIAN DEPOSITS Aeolian deposits such as sand dunes and dust are those transported and laid down by wind. Sand accumulations form principally at the fore edge of marine terraces as long, linear beach ridges, and against old sea cliffs. The sand probably was derived from an active beach at the time. Or it may have come when sea level dropped and exposed the broad, sandy abrasion platform, allowing the wind to pick up and blow the sand inland from the previously submerged marine shelf. In many areas of southern California, sand is also derived from the mouths of major rivers, so the San Diego River may have provided an additional source in the northern part of the peninsula.

Beach ridges form at the top of sea cliffs. During onshore flow of an air mass, the air must speed up at the sea cliff as it moves onshore. You'll commonly feel a strong breeze at the top of a sea cliff, only to have the breeze die down as you move away from the edge of the cliff. Sand that becomes airborne during strong wind conditions can be transported up the sea cliff, only to drop out of suspension as soon as the air velocity dies off away from the edge of the cliff. Thus, sand accumulates parallel to the coast and sea cliff as a long, linear mound. Beach ridges are common features in San Diego, especially in North County, and they are present from Ocean Beach southward to the Point Loma area on the lower marine terraces.

Windblown dust is a common occurrence on Point Loma, but the dust rarely accumulates rapidly enough to constitute an actual deposit. Instead, silt-sized dust tends to be incorporated into the soils of the region, adding nutrients and increasing the soil's ability to retain moisture.

COLLUVIAL DEPOSITS Colluvium is the accumulation of soil material near the bottoms of slopes that is transported primarily by gravitational processes and local erosion. These deposits can reach tens of feet thick under the right conditions, such as at the bases of ancient, abandoned sea cliffs. At Point Loma, colluvium also accumulates at the base of road cuts and near the headscarps of old landslides.

Common, tell-tale signs of this downslope movement include tilted sign posts, telephone poles, fences, or even trees. The surface material moves fastest, with the velocity of soil movement decreasing with depth.

IRON PISOLITHS

Iron pisoliths are easy to find. A common stop on geology field trips begins at the small parking lot where Osprey Street meets Sunset Cliffs Boulevard. Walking down the slope toward the coast, people find that the nearly spherical pieces act like ball bearings under the feet, causing them to slip and slide.

SOILS Soil is the weathering profile that develops in alluvium and rock over time. The expression of any soil is a function of many important factors including type and abundance of local vegetation, slope aspect and other topographic factors, the nature of the material into which the soil is developed, climate, and time. Many of these factors have changed during the past several hundred thousand years, so soils must be viewed as the complex end product of these and other factors, as well as changes in them over time.

Generally, the soils of Point Loma can be grouped into three categories: those developed in rock, in alluvium, and in thick aeolian sand deposits. Most of the soils are relatively old (80,000 to several 100,000 years in age), giving sufficient time to weather the original minerals. During weathering, iron is released from existing minerals, as well as from those introduced by windblown dust. When exposed to air, iron oxides form, which tend to impart a reddish hue to the soil; most of this iron accumulates below the organically enriched top soil.

Some Point Loma soils possess a distinctive accumulation of iron pisoliths, or concretions. Specifically, the soils that developed in the thick, sandy aeolian deposits have a shallow subsurface horizon that is commonly loaded with small (1/4- to 1/2-inch-sized) sandstone spheres that are cemented with iron. These pisoliths are believed to have formed primarily under conifers during the Pleistocene, when it was cooler and rainfall was higher than today. Thus, all the Point Loma localities that still have these types of soils are relics from the Pleistocene, when pine trees were far more extensive along the coast and conditions were more similar to those of central California today.

TIDE SHOWS

Low tides draw crowds of people to the tidepools in Cabrillo National Monument, coming to see the array of marine animals and plants that inhabit the pools. As they find and identify various invertebrates, they walk on Cretaceous sandstone and mudstone beds that display the burrows, tracks, and grazing marks made by invertebrates 76 to 72 million years ago.

TIDEPOOLS Tidepools along the rocky shore form where uneven erosion has left depressions and clefts in the resistant bedrock-abrasion platform. They are best seen at low tides, especially during minus tides.

Tidepools have their own distinct marine life, quite different from the animals usually found along open-coast sandy beaches—many types of mollusks, for instance, that require attachment to hard surfaces. Some organisms actively erode and sculpt the rock surfaces.

SEA CLIFF EROSION Ocean waves beating on the sea cliffs of Point Loma have caused significant retreat of the cliffs. The lighthouse is clearly visible between outliers of the Cretaceous middle submarine fan over-

The classic "Lovers Leap" photo shows a couple on Point Loma about 1898 with the lighthouse in the background.

bank deposits in the classic "Lover's Leap" photograph taken around the year 1898. A modern picture taken from a similar position reveals the same lighthouse but very different beach cliffs. In this area, ocean waves have eroded the sea cliffs landward several tens of feet, prompting placement of large rocks to try to slow the rate of erosion.

At Sunset Cliffs the Bird Rock terrace is locally preserved at about 20 to 25 feet in elevation, but the prominent surface on which much of the expensive real estate is built is the 120,000-

A century later, the lighthouse remains but the aesthetic sea-stack topography has been destroyed by ocean waves. Large boulders have been dumped onto the shoreline as riprap to slow erosional retreat of the sea cliffs.

In this 1923 photo, a decorative bridge accentuates the natural beauty of sea cliffs below the Spalding estate at the end of Osprey Street. The rectangular cove formed when the roof of an elongated sea cave collapsed.

year-old Nestor terrace and its associated beach ridge.

Much of the sea cliff erosion along Sunset Cliffs takes place via the growth and collapse of sea caves. The process may be viewed in all developmental stages at a single stop, such as in the sea cliffs at the foot of Osprey Street.

When the Cretaceous sedimentary rocks were uplifted, they responded to stresses in part by fracturing. There are two prominent sets of fractures, or cracks, oriented N 30° to 40° E and N 40° to 50° W. Close inspection reveals some long, continuous joint fractures in the rock. Some are so narrow that a credit card cannot be inserted into them, while others have been eroded into large sea caves. The fractures are eroded when ocean waves slam against the sea cliffs pushing water in and out of the joints thus widening them. These wider joints can accommodate sand and gravel that waves then push back and forth as an abrasive, further widening the joints. As waves constantly push

Ocean-wave attack not only destroyed the 1923 development but so scared this generation that they dumped riprap into the cove to slow erosion, drastically reducing the natural beauty.

into the joints, they become even wider and deeper, forming small caves. Continued growth can form caves more than 100 feet long and 30 feet wide. When a cave grows too big, pieces of the roof will collapse, forming blowholes. As more years pass, entire cave roofs will collapse, creating rectangular coves with pocket beaches.

In 1928 the view northward along Sunset Cliffs from southwest of Novara Street featured several sea stacks. The Spalding house at Osprey and Sunset Cliffs Boulevard is visible in the upper left.

The rectangular cove formed by the collapse of a sea cave near the bottom of Osprey Street was aesthetically enhanced by an arched bridge and fences as shown in a 1923 photograph. A modern picture shot from a similar position shows the same cove modified by erosion.

Sea cliff erosion may also be gauged by comparing photographs taken from the promontory jutting into the ocean between Novara and Monaco streets. The sea stacks, rock masses standing above sea level, so prominent in 1928 are long gone today.

Many lovely coves have been destroyed in the name of coastal protection by filling them with riprap (large boulders) and building cement walls. Though these efforts may slow the rate of erosion somewhat, they severely diminish the beauty and uniqueness of the cliffs.

Geology sets the stage for all of Point Loma's life. The land —its rock, soils, and topography—forms the foundation upon which all the animal and plant life has developed. And as the next chapter will show, the life of

This 2001 photo shows how wave erosion has removed the land occupied by the photographer in 1928. A similar northward view reveals a changed coastline, but with the Spalding house still visible in the upper left.

Point Loma is also significantly shaped by climate and the effects of the ocean.

REFERENCES/ADDITIONAL READING

Abbott, Patrick L. 1999. *The Rise and Fall of San Diego.* Sunbelt Publications, San Diego. Explains 150 million years of geologic history in San Diego, including Point Loma. Winner of San Diego Book Awards best new book in category of San Diego & Environs.

Abbott, Patrick L., ed. 1984. *Upper Cretaceous depositional systems, southern California—northern Baja California: Pacific Section, Society of Economic Paleontologists and Mineralogists,* book 36, 140 pp. Numerous papers describing aspects of the Cretaceous geology of Point Loma.

Kennedy, Michael P. 1973. Sea-cliff erosion at Sunset Cliffs, San Diego. *California Geology,* v. 26, pp. 27–31. Diagrams and explanations of how sea cliffs retreat at Sunset Cliffs.

Kennedy, Michael P. 1975. *Geology of the San Diego metropolitan area, California: Section A—Del Mar, La Jolla, and Point Loma 7.5 minute quadrangles: California Division of Mines and Geology Bulletin 200.* The most detailed geologic maps, printed in color on top of a base map showing streets and their names.

Kern, J. Philip and John E. Warme. 1974. Trace fossils and bathymetry of the Upper Cretaceous Point Loma Formation, San Diego, California. *Geological Society of America Bulletin,* v. 85, pp. 893–900. Detailed analysis of burrows and tracks in the Cretaceous rocks exposed in the tidepools of Cabrillo National Monument.

Kern, J. Philip and Thomas K. Rockwell. 1992. Chronology and deformation of Quaternary marine shorelines, San Diego County, California. In *Quaternary Coasts of the United States: Society of Economic Paleontologists and Mineralogists, Special Publication* 48, pp. 377–382. The most detailed analysis of the positions and ages of prehistoric shorelines in the San Diego region.

Lindvall, Scott C. and Thomas K. Rockwell. 1995. Holocene activity of the Rose Canyon fault zone in San Diego, California: *Journal of Geophysical Research,* v. 100, no. B12, pp. 24, 121–124, 132. The most important paper dealing with the Rose Canyon fault.

The Highs and the Lows: Climate and Oceanography

At a latitude of about 33 degrees North, the San Diego region is favored with a moderate, subtropical and, many say, ideal climate. Annual average temperature is 63 degrees Fahrenheit, mean rainfall measures 10 inches, there are 146 clear days with 117 more only partly cloudy. The cool waters of the Pacific Ocean greatly moderate coastal weather. Without this control, the average temperature, especially along the coast, would be much hotter.

Weather records, including temperature, barometric pressure, and rainfall, exist for San Diego at least since 1850. Average weather conditions at Point Loma match those observed at Lindbergh Field Airport, where San Diego's official weather records have been kept since 1914.

January is the coolest, rainiest month, with low temperatures averaging about 48 degrees F and precipitation of about 2 inches. June, July, and August are the hottest, driest months, with an average rainfall of less than 0.1 inch in each month. This is the moderate-temperature and sensible-rainfall "climate" San Diego residents and visitors expect.

Yet, as Lazarus Long remarked in Robert Heinlein's *Time Enough for Love*, "Climate is what you expect, weather is what you get." A key feature of San Diego's weather is variability—from drought and flood, to freezing and parching, from day to day, month to month, and year to year. For all its ideal weather, San Diego has experienced some amazing extremes over the past 150 years. On September 26, 1963, when autumn temperatures are normally about 70 degrees F, the scorching high of 111 degrees F was an immense surprise.

AUTHOR

Dr. Reinhard E. Flick is Staff Oceanographer for the California Department of Boating and Waterways, stationed at the Scripps Institution of Oceanography in La Jolla, California.

The daily average maximum (red) and minimum (blue) temperatures, and the daily extreme high and low temperatures, measured at Lindbergh Field from 1914 to 2000. Average highest temperature is 76° F in August, while the average lowest temperature is 48° F in January.

Average and extreme rainfall for each day of the year as measured at Lindbergh Field. The highest amount of rainfall occurs in January, with a mean of about 2 inches. Summers, on average, are very dry, with only about 0.5 inch of rain falling from May through September.

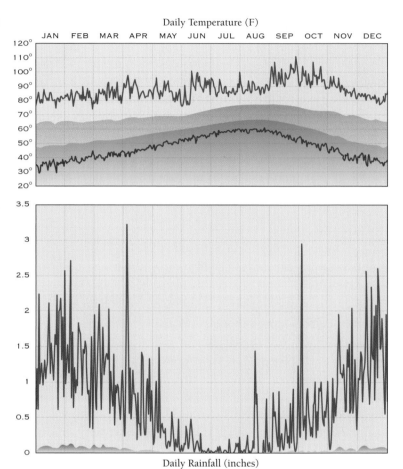

Daily Temperature (F)

Daily Rainfall (inches)

That day was the peak of the worst heat wave in San Diego's history: It was 95 degrees F at 8:00 AM; the temperature stayed above 90 degrees F for eleven hours and above 100 degrees F for seven hours; relative humidity was a parched 6% compared with the average of 69%. And during April, San Diegans are prepared for the showers that produce an average of about 0.8 inch of rain for the month. But someone here on April 5, 1926, would have been astonished by the 3.2 inches of rain that poured down *on that single day*—four times the amount that falls during an entire typical April!

SAN DIEGO'S WEATHER

Weather conditions at Point Loma are essentially those of coastal San Diego, with a few local quirks. Conditions in San Diego, in turn, reflect those of southern California. The region's large-scale meteorological conditions are dominated by the semipermanent Eastern Pacific high pressure system, and the southern California–Arizona low pressure area, or "trough." The high is produced by cool, sinking air over large parts of the eastern Pacific Ocean, while the low results from hot, dry air rising over the southwestern deserts.

The two dominant meteorological conditions in southern California—the Eastern Pacific High pressure system and the southern California-Arizona low pressure area.

Atmospheric circulation around the high produces the large-scale winds that blow, on average, along the coast from the northwest. The local wind regime also has an onshore component. In fact, on a day-to-day basis, most of the wind motion is associated with the daily sea breeze that peaks at about 2:00 PM, weakens around sunset, and often blows offshore through the night. It is the longshore winds, though, that so profoundly affect coastal oceanographic conditions by contributing to upwelling: the rise of deeper, colder waters to the surface in the coastal ocean.

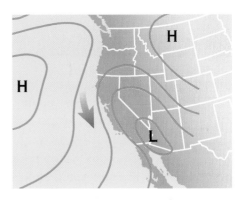

SUMMER In summer, broadly defined as the months of April through September, both the Pacific high and the desert trough intensify, grow, and move north. The high pressure pattern essentially steers any Pacific weather fronts arriving at the coast far to the north of San Diego. Meanwhile, the contrast between the high and low pressure areas produces persistent coastal winds from the north and northwest. In fact, except during winter storms, coastal winds are actually slightly stronger and steadier during summer than during winter. Over the past thirty years, average wind velocities during summer were 7.6 miles an hour from the west-northwest. However, gusts of up to 40 miles an hour, generally from the west, have occurred during summer months.

Summer is also known as "stratus season," or more popularly as "June gloom," because coastal clouds and fog are heaviest. The low-lying stratus clouds are the most common type observed in San Diego. Stratus forming at ground level is simply fog, and fog obscures visibility in coastal areas. It's also associated with the marine layer, a thin blanket of chilly, moist air formed over the cool waters off the coast and blown ashore by the onshore breeze. The layer is trapped from above by air sinking around the eastern fringe of the Pacific High. It shields the coast from the high temperatures of the descending air mass, but not inland areas, thus explaining the drastic temperature difference between cool beach areas and much hotter inland parts of San Diego.

Summer mornings are often characterized by low-lying coastal clouds popularly known as "June gloom."

The marine layer generally intensifies at night and dissipates during the day, leading to the generic San Diego coastal weather forecast of "night and morning low clouds, with clearing by early afternoon." As the marine layer grows and descends during evening hours, it first obscures the upper levels of Point Loma and then eventually spills over to cover more of San Diego. This is the phenomenon that most thought led to mariners' complaints about the old Point Loma lighthouse so often being obscured by fog, and that quickly caused the light to be moved closer to sea level.

Occasionally, the fog doesn't clear during the daytime. This is likely due to a phenomenon called the Catalina Eddy, a huge whirl in the upper-level air flow over the Southern California Bight, centered around Catalina Island. The eddy is a result of

As soon as the first lighthouse was built at the top of Point Loma in 1855, mariners complained that the light was too seldom visible. A number of ships were lost, and the assumption was that clouds and fog obscured the light. In 1891, a new lighthouse was built on the low-lying coastal terrace below the old lighthouse, and it is visible over the water much more of the time. Yet some doubt has been cast on the belief that weather and climate were the only, or even the main, reasons the old lighthouse failed its duty.

Information pertinent to flight operations at North

POINT LOMA LIGHTHOUSE IN LATE 1800'S

Island, just east across the entrance to San Diego Bay, may help explain. Statistics on visibility and "ceiling" height—the elevation of the cloud base—indicate that regardless of visibility, the ceiling height is above 500 feet (the elevation of the old Point Loma light is 462 feet) an average of about 97%

of the time on an annual basis, and more than 94% of the time even during June. Visibility can be obscured even when the ceiling is high. But, when the ceiling is higher than 500 feet, visibility on average is greater than 3 nautical miles over 93% of the time annually, and about 91% of the time during June. These statistics cast doubt on the idea that the old Point Loma light was not seen purely because of frequent poor visibility and low cloud cover. More likely, the flat, horizontal beam produced by the old lighthouse simply shone much too high to be consistently visible from sea level.

suddenly reach Point Conception, where the coast takes a sharp eastward turn. The wind continues to move south, but also spreads and starts to curl up to the east as it fills the gap over the Bight. The result is a rapid thickening of the marine layer which lowers coastal air temperatures and can spread clouds and fog into inland areas during intense events.

WINTER As with summer, average winter weather conditions typify San Diego's mild and desirable climate. The mean temperature for January is 56 degrees F, with a mean daily minimum of 48 degrees F. Even the 29-degree record low temperature, which occurred on January 4, 1949, is enviable by Midwest or northeast United States standards. Rainfall records provide a similar picture. January and February—the wettest months in San Diego—see on average about 2 inches of rain each. Furthermore, winter rainfall generally is confined to a few days when weather systems are passing through; between storms, skies are usually clear. Average wind velocities during winter are 7.5 miles an hour, generally blowing from the northwest.

Two major winter weather scenarios, with their variations, describe almost all the typical cases in San Diego. These are high-pressure-dominated, offshore wind conditions, and times of low-pressure trough or frontal passage. The high-pressure condition produces clear and often warm weather in southern California, while the low pressure is associated with stormy, more winterlike weather. Obviously the first weather pattern dominates San Diego's winter climate, on average, because even in January the sun shines about 70% of the time. The second pattern makes the region's weather interesting, and in some cases, exciting.

High Pressure During the winter months, broadly defined as October through March, the East Pacific high pressure system and the southern California–Arizona low pressure trough weaken and move to the south. In winter, two other pressure systems enter the southern California weather picture—the Aleutian Low, which spawns storms in the Gulf of Alaska, and the Great Basin High and associated West Coast high pressure ridge. The position of these systems determines the track of the mid-latitude jet stream and the path of north Pacific storms impacting the West Coast. Winter weather in San Diego, as in all of southern California, is largely determined by the relative location of these two large pressure centers and the resulting storm tracks.

The Great Basin high pressure system, which often develops

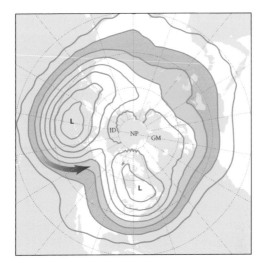

over the deserts of Utah and Colorado, is associated with a clockwise or anticyclonic flow which can produce offshore winds in southern California. This system deflects winter storms to the north. This atmospheric configuration is very stable, and results in a jet stream path that forecasters refer to as an 'Ω' pattern, for the shape of the Greek letter omega. If this high is strong and persistent, it is difficult for storms to penetrate toward the coast of southern California. Drought conditions can result if the condition redevelops over a number of winters. But mostly, the resulting weak or moderate offshore winds produce those familiar beautiful, clear San Diego winter days.

The Aleutian Low, above, and the Great Basin High, below, are two pressure systems that most affect winter weather.

When the Great Basin High is very strong, with a trough of low pressure existing over the California–Arizona desert, intense winds from the northeast or east may begin developing in southern California. When their speed exceeds about 30 miles an hour, these winds

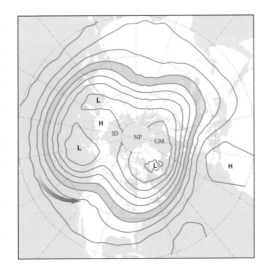

are called "Santa Anas." Santa Anas are most prevalent between October and February. Wind blasts are especially strong through the canyons, with gusts that have exceeded 100 miles an hour. As the air masses descend the coastal mountain ranges, they warm through compression by about 5 degrees F for each 1,000-foot drop. These desert air masses are typically dry to start with, and this heating lowers their relative humidity even more. For this reason, Santa Ana winds often sear the southern California coast, and in arid winters the fire hazard increases all over southern California. The strongest winds usually occur during the night and morning hours, whereas the sea breeze moderates Santa Ana conditions during the late morning and afternoon.

Frontal Passage Besides the obviously cooler temperatures, the main attribute that distinguishes winter from summer in San Diego is the passage of storm fronts and the influence of low-pressure troughs. Fronts simply show stronger pressure gradients and swifter changes in surface weather than do troughs. Forecasters distinguish several discrete types of low-pressure systems because each is associated with different weather characteristics: a Nevada low, a cutoff low, and a migratory low with either dry or wet fronts.

The Nevada low is a low-pressure condition that can develop in late winter or early spring over southern Nevada. It often brings cold and gusty onshore winds over southern California but seldom causes rain. A slow-moving, cutoff low-pressure trough sometimes develops off the coast of southern California when a mass of cold air becomes "cut off" from its high-latitude source. This can persist for several weeks, especially if trapped between a simultaneously occurring East Pacific high pressure system, and a Midwestern blocking high. Under certain circumstances, enough moisture can be entrained to produce moderate to heavy rain for up to two days in San Diego.

Most low-pressure systems moving through San Diego are

dry and produce no rain, but in winter they often show high or mid-level clouds. Nevertheless, migratory lows and their associated storm fronts produce most of the winterlike weather observed in San Diego. These systems increase in strength from November through March, while the associated clouds and rain often push farther south as winter progresses. Winter low-pressure systems approach from the southwest, west, or northwest, and their direction often determines what kind of weather they bring.

The southwest types can foster some of the heaviest rains observed in San Diego because of the moisture content they

Winter low-pressure systems approaching from the southwest have historically brought heavy and sometimes damaging rains to San Diego.

gather as they pass over warm, tropical waters. Rains from these systems often continue for thirty-six to forty-eight hours and are preceded by heavy cloud layers approaching from the southwest. Winter storm systems approaching from the west are often associated with a broad, mid-latitude eastern Pacific area of low pressure. These storms are usually so large that they also produce rain in San Diego for up to a few days. The western-approaching fronts transport a moderate amount of mois-

This 1916 photograph shows flood damage at Old Town.

ture from lower latitudes, but also draw in cold air from higher latitudes. This combination frequently produces heavy rains in southern California.

Variability in Winter Weather Variation in winter weather conditions has always been a prominent feature of San Diego's climate, and winter is the season when strong weather variations are most conspicuous from one year to the next, and over several decades. The climate is greatly influenced by conditions over the Pacific Ocean. Winter storms that affect the region generally originate in the North Pacific or Gulf of Alaska and follow paths that depend on the relative position of the Aleutian low and Pacific high. During winters when high pressure prevails along the West Coast, storms are deflected northward into Canada and Alaska. When the high-pressure cell moves to the south and west, storm trajectories shift south toward the coasts of Oregon and California.

The long rainfall record available in San Diego lets us examine interannual variation in storminess—the number and intensity of storms impacting the region. Average rainfall has been about 10 inches per year, or about 0.8 inch per month, over the 1850 to early 2000 record available from the National Climate Data Center. The monthly figures are used to calculate "cumulative residual precipitation," a much "smoother" series that emphasizes wet and dry intervals that persist for several years or longer.

The cumulative residual rainfall curve dropped steadily from 1850 to about 1880. This was followed by a sudden jump in the 1880s including 1883–1884, one of the worst flood winters in San Diego history. The highest total monthly rainfall was 9.26 inches, in December 1921. Another wet and stormy winter occurred in 1940–1941, close to the culmination of a prolonged period of wetter-than-average weather that began around 1906.

The years 1946 to 1977 were a prolonged dry period of below average rainfall, punctuated with occasional wet winters

(1951–1952, 1957–1958, and 1965–1966). This relatively benign thirty-year period of mild weather prevailed in all of central and southern California, and corresponded with the time of intense coastal development and population increase following World War II, especially in the south. This may account for the surprise many people expressed during the run of stormy winters that began suddenly in 1978 in southern California.

Beginning in 1978 and through 1983, winters were wet and stormy, and this continued throughout most of the 1990s. These winters included the "Miracle March" of 1983, with 6.6 inches of rain, January 1993 with 9.1 inches, and January 1995 with 8.1 inches. There is an especially sharp jump in 1998, which reflects the 12.5 inches of rainfall between January and March 1998, during the El Niño winter of 1997–1998.

Tree-ring widths, sediments, and other long-term proxy rainfall records show that several decades of dry weather followed by somewhat shorter periods of above-average rainfall have been the standard pattern of climate variability in California and throughout the Southwest for many centuries. Research into both interannual and long-term variability of oceanographic conditions points to the importance of the Pacific Ocean in governing California's weather patterns. Two large-scale, multiyear oceanographic and atmospheric fluctuations seem to set the stage for either stormy, normal, or dry weather in San Diego. These are El Niño and the Pacific Decadal Oscillation.

EL NIÑO El Niño, and sister La Niña, have become household names in many parts of the world affected by the extremes of drought or rain associated with their most mischievous incarnations. The El Niño winters of 1982–1983 and 1997–1998 stand out in recent memory, not only for their stormy weather with high rainfalls and large waves, but also because of the high ocean water temperatures. These resulted in widespread species redistributions, including tropical fish caught off northern California, and massive kelp mortality from wave action and lack of nutrients. A parody of these names, "La Nada," has been used to describe the relatively noneventful winters of 1999–2000, and 2000–2001.

EL NIÑO & LA NIÑA

El Niño is a state of the ocean and atmosphere in the tropical Pacific Ocean. It appears every two to seven years with various strengths, and lasts six to eighteen months. El Niño is characterized by higher-than-normal sea surface temperatures and sea levels along the west coast of South America, weaker or reversed trade winds over the tropical Pacific, and a shift of the intense convection and associated rainfall away from Australia and Indonesia toward the eastern tropical Pacific. Ocean warming off South America strongly inhibits the normal upwelling, decimating fisheries. The most severe symptoms of El Niño events were often first noted off the Peruvian coast around Christmas, hence the Spanish name which means "the child," or specifically the "Christ child." La Niña is a state of the tropical Pacific and atmosphere that presents essentially the opposite characteristics. Barometric pressure swings across the South Pacific give rise to the name El Niño Southern Oscillation, often abbreviated as ENSO.

El Niño is a tropical phenomenon with strong effects in mid-latitudes, including southern California. The intense convective transfer of heat from the equatorial ocean into the atmosphere during strong El Niño events produces more and stronger storm systems across the entire North Pacific Ocean. The ocean warming off the South American coast spreads thousands of miles north and south in a matter of months, warming the waters off southern California by up to 10 degrees F above normal. In contrast, during La Niña episodes, Pacific storminess is much less severe and coastal ocean temperatures much lower.

About two-thirds of El Niño events are associated with above-average storminess and the attendant rainfall and high waves along southern California. The difference lies in the path that North Pacific storms take, and this in turn depends on the relative location of the large high- and low-pressure systems during the winter months. During El Niño episodes, these pressure systems are enhanced, leading to more frequent and more vigorous storm activity over the Pacific. But the storm tracks still depend on the position of the pressure systems.

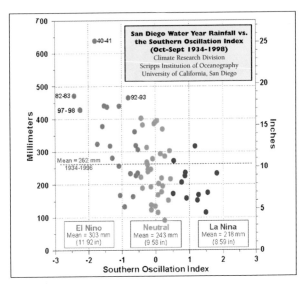

During the El Niño winter of 1976–1977, for example, storm tracks were wound tightly to the north, leaving California in the midst of a drought. In contrast, during the severe El Niño winter in 1982–1983, several clusters of storms caused more than $100 million in damage in coastal California.

Strong correlations of El Niño and high waves on the southern California coast have also been noted. For example, a wave intensity study showed that from 1984 to 1995, a period of almost continuous El Niño conditions, there were three times as many events with waves higher than 13 feet than in the decade before. Interestingly, the number of waves exceeding 20 feet during 1984–1995 failed to reach the total during the "super El Niño" of 1982–1983. During El Niño years, wave approach angles also shift south, so that large waves often attack from due west.

The relationship of rainfall in San Diego to the existence of warm El Niño (red), cool La Niña (blue), or neutral (green) conditions. A wide range of seasonal rainfall totals are observed for El Niño states. Mainly below-average rainfall occurred during La Niña periods, with only two years of above-average rainfall.

PACIFIC DECADAL OSCILLATION PDO is a relatively new concept that arose from study of sea-surface temperature records throughout the Pacific Ocean. The dominant mode of variability turns out to be a swing between warm tropical ocean tempera-

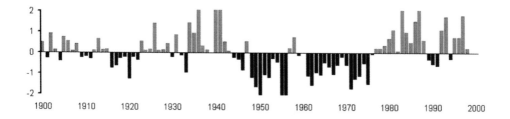

The monthly Pacific Decadal Oscillation index from 1900 to 2000. While the beginning of the record is fuzzy, one and one half cycles of warm-cool-warm clearly appear between 1920 and 2000. Warm conditions prevailed from 1925-1946, and from 1977 through the late 1990s, with cool conditions from 1947-1976.

tures and cold mid-latitudes, called the "warm phase," and the opposite condition, called the "cool phase." The PDO shares some behavior with El Niño, but also has two crucial differences. First, El Niño typically lasts up to eighteen months, while PDO cycles persist for twenty or thirty years. Second, El Niño is a tropical occurrence with mid-latitude effects, while the PDO is exactly the opposite—a mid-latitude condition with secondary effects in the tropics. Just as warm El Niño events increase storminess in the North Pacific, warm-phase PDO conditions do the same, while cool phases are associated with a decrease in storm activity over the North Pacific.

As in the long-term variations in the rainfall patterns over San Diego, there was a major climate shift in 1977 that brought increased storminess to southern California. The implication from the PDO index is that the climate may have undergone another shift, back to the cool phase after the 1998 El Niño. This would imply a decrease in storminess, less beach erosion, and less stress on kelp and intertidal communities. Only the future will tell if this variation comes to pass.

OCEANOGRAPHY

The Pacific Ocean's most important influence on southern California, including San Diego and Point Loma, is its moderating effect on the region's weather. Other notable ocean-atmosphere effects include El Niño and the Pacific Decadal Oscillation. Specific oceanographic variables that influence the habitat and coastal resources of Point Loma include sea level, especially the regular rhythm of the tides, and the impact of waves.

SEA LEVEL Several factors contribute to the instantaneous height of sea level. The tide is the largest, and only, component that is predictable. Storm surges, large-scale changes in water temperature, wind-driven circulation, and climate-related El Niño events also influence coastal water levels in California. All of these raise or lower sea level for some characteristic length of time from hours to years, and therefore directly or indirectly affect the intertidal habitat. The rising mean sea level may become increasingly important in the future, especially if there is an acceleration of the modest rate of rise of about 9 inches per century observed in San Diego over the past seventy-five years. Rising sea level tends to push habitat zones landward. If the rate of rise is too high, or if the landward shift of species and habitats is blocked, these habitats may be lost.

Point Loma's nearshore environments are heavily impacted by the effects of sea level variability and wave action.

Annual mean sea level records from San Francisco, available since 1854, suggest that the rate of rise on the California coast may be greater after about 1930 than it was before. We don't know yet if this apparent increase in the rate of sea level rise has any relation to global warming, or even if it is confined to the San Francisco Bay region (although Seattle shows a similar pattern). Nevertheless, there is much speculation about future sea level rise.

If the trend observed over the past seventy-five years continues unchanged, sea levels would be about 0.38 feet higher by 2050, and 0.75 feet higher by 2100. Other estimates of future sea level rise have been made by the National Academy of Science, which stated that by the year 2100 global sea level will likely be 1.6 to 3.3 feet higher than it was in 1990. This suggests that the rate of rise may increase by a factor of two to four over the twenty-first century. The rise would not be linear but would accelerate, with greater increases later in the century. The academy study also outlined more drastic possibilities: the highest estimate (from a credible source) of future sea level elevation is 11.5 feet higher by 2100. However, this figure assumes a large contribution of water from collapse of the Antarctic Ice Sheet, an event deemed unlikely during this century.

Tides Logically, the most important physical oceanographic factor affecting tidepools is the tide. Tides are the regular changes of ocean water levels caused by the gravitational forces among the moon, sun, and Earth, *and* the response of the water in the ocean to these forces. Because of the astronomical motions involved, and Earth's rotation, most tidal oscillations appear

READING THE TIDES

Tidal elevations are referenced to the Mean Lower Low Water (MLLW) datum. This is calculated as the average elevation of all the observed lower-low water readings for each day in a given 19-year period. Nineteen years corresponds to the nearest whole number of years to the 18.6-year lunar node cycle, the longest period astronomical variation of any practical significance. The current tidal "epoch" is 1983–2001. MLLW is commonly used as the datum for tide calendars, as well as for indicating depths on navigation charts.

in bands around one and two cycles per lunar day (24 hours, 50 minutes), respectively called "diurnal" and "semidiurnal" tides.

On the California coast, the tides are mixed, containing nearly equal measures of diurnal and semidiurnal components. This combination gives rise to characteristic patterns of high tide, low tide, and tide range over time that have important consequences for the coast, including the intertidal zone. The two high tides and two low tides that occur each day along the California coast are, respectively, unequal in amplitude. This is the most noticeable feature of a mixed tide. The prominent fluctuations of the high tides on this coast occur daily, twice monthly, twice yearly, every 4.4 years, and every 18.6 years.

The average tide range in San Diego Bay is 4 feet, while the extreme range is 10 feet; these are at the Navy Pier near downtown, where the official tide gauge measurements have been made since 1906. The tide along the open coast, however, is nearly 10% smaller and more accurately reflected by measurements made since 1924 at the Scripps Institution of Oceanography Pier in La Jolla. The average tide range along the coast, including at Point Loma, is about 3.7 feet, with extreme values of about 9.2 feet.

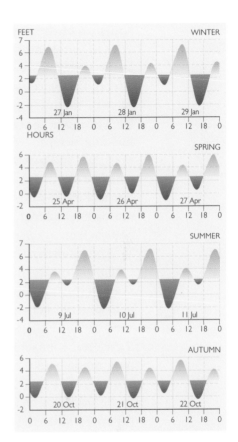

The curves show typical tides in San Diego for a few days each during the winter, spring, summer, and autumn of 1983, a time of especially high tide ranges.

Monthly tidal changes are dominated by the spring-neap cycle, with two periods of relatively high tides (springs) around full and new moon, and two periods of lower ranges (neaps) around the times of half moon. One spring tide range per month is usually higher than the other on this coast, a consequence of the moon's distance and declination. The highest tides in the winter and summer months are higher than those in the spring and fall as a result of lunar and solar declination effects. Furthermore, the extreme monthly higher-high tides in the winter tend to occur in the morning, sometimes quite early, but they occur in the afternoon during summer. From a coastal flooding perspective, this is a disadvantage because preparations for winter storm waves often must be made at night, in anticipation of the high tide the following morning. But for tidepool inhabitants it is an advantage because the water level during hot summer afternoons is higher than it would be if this pattern were reversed.

Longer-period variations also occur in the tides. On the California coast, there is a distinct 4.4-year cycle that results in higher maximum monthly tides of about 0.5 feet, compared with years in between. This cycle peaked in 1982–1983, 1986–1987, 1990–1991, 1995–1996, and 1999–2000, and will continue thereafter. A smaller 18.6-year cycle is also apparent and raises peak tides about 0.2 feet.

Storm Surge   Storm surge is the difference between the observed water level and the predicted tide, due to the effects of atmospheric (barometric) pressure and wind. When the atmospheric pressure drops during a storm, the water surface is pushed up. Each millibar drop in pressure causes a 0.4-inch rise in water level. Both the onshore and longshore components of wind velocity during storms may also contribute to coastal storm surges.

Compared with the East and Gulf coasts of the United States, storm surges in southern California are small, reaching a maximum value of about 1 foot. This is due to the near absence of hurricanes on this coast, and the relatively narrow continental shelf that drops off sharply to deep ocean close to shore. The maximum observed storm-related surge in southern California occurred in early February 1998 during an intense storm, and peaked at about 1.2 feet. Together with high tides and storm surge, wave surges can cause coastal erosion. These effects also expose the upper intertidal areas to wave stresses during storms.

WAVES Waves provide nearly all the energy input that drives shoreline processes along the California coast. For Point Loma in particular, waves relentlessly impact the cliffs, tidepools, and pocket beaches. Without the constantly breaking waves, this shoreline would have a totally different character. While erosion problems might not be such a pressing concern, the stresses on the intertidal habitat would also be much less, and the types and numbers of creatures would be entirely different.

The intense motion of breaking waves imparts large forces on land forms and structures. Along with the direct effects of individual breakers, waves sometimes produce a strong long-shore current that flows parallel to the beach and that can move sand along the coast. Wave action can also generate longer-period motions that are amplified at the sloping shoreline of beaches, even as the waves that generate them are dissipated. These "surf beat" oscillations can be quite high, especially during very energetic storm surf, and are the leading cause of beach berm overtopping and coastal flooding in southern California.

Understanding the effects of waves is a key element to understanding and dealing with coastal processes in southern California. The Pacific Ocean, the largest ocean in the world, has plenty of space, or "fetch," for storms to generate high and long waves. If the storms are far from land, the waves can travel over enormous distances to reach this coast. Such waves are called "swell," as opposed to locally generated waves called "seas." Swell waves usually have a longer period interval between crests, and have cleaner form and more organized appearance than seas, which have shorter crests and are more confused. Measurements reveal that over 80% of the energy in the southern California wave climate is in the form of waves with periods of 5 seconds and longer. During times of large waves, this fraction reaches 90% and is dominated by swell.

Wave Sources Incoming waves along the southern California coast are of three types: northern hemisphere swell, southern hemisphere swell, and seas generated locally. Waves in the swell categories originate in their respective hemispheres north and south of the equator, arriving in southern California after traveling impressive distances.

Northern hemisphere swell waves are usually produced by a specific, remote meteorological disturbance, including Aleutian storms, subtropical storms north of Hawaii, Pacific typhoons, tropical hurricanes, and strong winds in the eastern North Pacific. Aleutian storms move from west to east across the Pacific at high latitude and often stagnate in the Gulf of Alaska. These waves reach the southern California coast, but with diminished amplitude because of the shoreline orientation and blocking by Point Conception and the offshore Channel Islands. During occasional winters and springs, such as in 1982–1983, the storm tracks of these extratropical cyclones are displaced farther south than normal. This produces maximum wave heights in central and southern California, and is the most important source of extreme waves in the region.

Tropical hurricanes commonly develop at low latitudes off the west coast of Mexico during the months of July to October. They first move west and then curve north and northeast before dissipating in the colder waters off Baja California. The swell waves generated by these events usually do not exceed 6 feet in

Three categories of incoming waves along the southern California coast—northern hemisphere swell, southern hemisphere swell, and seas generated locally.

height by the time they reach southern California. On rare occasions, however, the offshore waters are warm enough to sustain a hurricane much farther north than normal. This happened in September 1939, when a hurricane passed directly over southern California. The resulting waves caused widespread destruction, especially on south-facing beaches.

Strong winds sometimes develop over the extreme eastern Pacific as a result of steep gradients in the atmospheric pressure around the Pacific high pressure cell. These strong and persistent north and northwest winds, an important feature of the summer weather pattern in California, also generate moderately high waves.

Southern hemisphere swell is generated in the South Pacific, Indian, and Southern oceans by high-latitude Antarctic and Pacific storms during the southern winter. The importance of an occasionally large southern swell was demonstrated by destructive waves that focused on the Long Beach breakwater in the 1950s. Southern swell provides the long, clean waves that are so popular among surfers during the summer months. These waves also cause reversals in the predominantly southward flow of sand on shore, and push the material to the north. During summer, these waves dominate the region's coastal processes simply because not enough compensating northern hemisphere swell is generated at that time.

Because "seas" are generated locally, forecasters need wind data from the area just upwind of the forecast location. In southern California, this can be up to several hundred miles offshore. Seas in the region are produced by storms sweeping through the area, by strong atmospheric pressure gradients that induce strong winds, or from daytime sea breezes. Winds vary over the Southern California Bight and are generally milder inside the islands and stronger and gustier offshore. This strong spatial variability together with the lack of measurements limits the accuracy of local wave predictions.

Swell height maps are routinely produced every few hours by the Scripps Institution of Oceanography (www.cdip.ucsd.edu).

Island Sheltering The Southern California Bight is noted for its offshore islands, shallow banks, canyons, and generally complicated bottom topography (bathymetry). Coastal orientation and the presence of islands and banks partially shelter southern California, including Point Loma, greatly influencing the swell propagating toward shore.

The coast along San Diego generally faces west, with the notable exception of Coronado and the tip of Point Loma, which are south-facing. Because of the complicated effects of bathymetry and island shadowing, the wave height at the shoreline is sensitive to relatively small changes in the incoming direction of the deep ocean waves. For the same reason, coastal wave heights can vary drastically over short distances along the shore. Small, local changes in shoreline orientation along

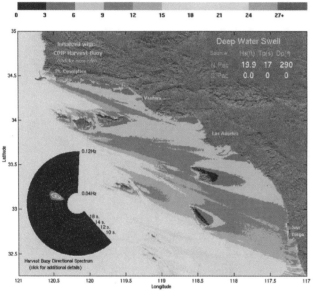

The map is based on measurements of wave height, period, and direction made at Harvest Buoy off Point Conception, and shows the wave height as a series of colors.

the west side of Point Loma can have dramatic effects on the wave exposure of these coastal segments. The east side of Point Loma is highly sheltered by the point itself, and only waves from the south, or those greatly reduced in size after wrapping around the tip by wave refraction, can enter San Diego Bay.

Point Loma's coastal climate, the effects of the Pacific Ocean, the force of waves, and the wetting and drying cycles of tides all give rise to highly adapted marine life. That nearshore environment features fascinating ecosystems, including tidepools on the rock shore and an extensive kelp forest offshore.

REFERENCES/ADDITIONAL READING

Diaz, H.F. and V. Markgraf. 1992. *El Niño, Historical and Paleoclimatic Aspects of the Southern Oscillation.* Cambridge University Press, Cambridge, UK. 476 pp.

Evans, T.E. III and D.A. Halvorson. 1998. *Climate of San Diego, California.* NOAA Technical Memorandum NWS WR-256. U.S. Department of Commerce, National Oceanic and Atmospheric Administration, National Weather Service, 89 pp.

Flick, R.E. 1993. The myth and reality of Southern California beaches, *Shore and Beach,* Journal of the American Shore and Beach Preservation Association 61 (3) 3–13.

Flick, R.E. 1998. Comparison of California tides, storm surges, and sea level during the El Niño winters of 1982–83 and 1997–98. *Shore and Beach,* Journal of the American Shore and Beach Preservation Association 66 (3) 7–11.

Graham, N.E. and H. F. Diaz. 2001. Evidence for intensification of North Pacific winter cyclones since 1948. *Bulletin American Meteorological Society* 82 (9) 1869–1893.

Mantua, N.J. et al. A Pacific interdecadal climate oscillation with impacts on salmon production. *Journal of the American Meteorological Society* 78 (6) 1069–1079.

National Academy of Sciences. 1990. *Sea-level Change.* National Research Council, Washington, D.C. 234 pp.

Naval Pacific Meteorology and Oceanography Facility San Diego. 1995. *Forecaster's Handbook for NAS North Island.* U.S. Navy Publication.

Pawka, S.S., D.L. Inman, and R.T. Guza. 1984. Island sheltering of surface gravity waves: Model and experiment. *Continental Shelf Research* 3 (1) 35–53.

Pugh, D.T. 1987. *Tides, Surges and Mean Sea-Level.* John Wiley and Sons, New York. 472 pp.

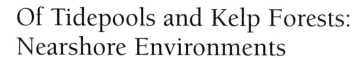

Of Tidepools and Kelp Forests: Nearshore Environments

San Diego was founded and, in many ways was built, around its marine resources. Juan Rodríguez Cabrillo, the first European to lay eyes on San Diego Bay in 1542, was impressed by the resources San Diego Bay had to offer. A later explorer, Sebastián Vizcaíno, described the naming of San Diego in 1602: *"The next day . . . we arrived at a port which must be the best to be found in all the South Sea, for, besides being protected on all sides and having good anchorage . . . it has very good wood and water, many fish of all kinds, many of which we caught with seine and hooks. . . .This port was given the name of San Diego."*

Both Cabrillo and Vizcaíno witnessed a place endowed with great marine natural resources—an abundance of fish and shellfish, a huge kelp forest, and most important to them, a large and well-protected natural harbor in the lee of Point Loma.

In the centuries that followed Cabrillo's arrival, marine resources would continue to attract people to San Diego. Early growth of the San Diego area was greatly accelerated once the focus of development was moved from Old Town to the shores of San Diego Bay. Twentieth-century growth was intimately linked to the U.S. Navy presence here, which was due to the quality of the bay as a port. San Diego Bay is now home port to seventy-five Naval ships, houses 8,500 commercial and recreational boat slips, and receives more than 700 commercial vessels each year. More than 35 million

AUTHORS

Bonnie J. Becker is a marine biologist with the National Park Service and a Ph.D. candidate at the Scripps Institution of Oceanography.

Dr. Mia Tegner was a research biologist at the Scripps Institution. She died in a diving accident in January 2001.

Dr. Paul Dayton is a Professor of Marine Ecology at the Scripps Institution of Oceanography.

Kelp beds

Nearshore
Intertidal

**Nearshore
communities of
Point Loma**

tourists visit the area yearly, many of whom come to enjoy the marine environment. As well, the city's surfers, fishermen, divers, kayakers, sailors, oceanographers, and amateur marine naturalists help to define the cultural feeling.

Since Cabrillo's arrival, the San Diego metropolitan area has grown into one of the ten largest cities in the United States, with 1.2 million residents according to the 2000 census. Therefore, any discussion of the marine resources of Point Loma, which is located within the city limits, must accept humans as an integral part of the system. For example, the bay is now the second-most toxic harbor in the nation, according to a 1998 study by the National Oceanic and Atmospheric Administration and the California State Water Resources Control Board. In addition, overharvesting, large-scale development, exotic species introductions, and shoreline modifications are potentially harmful activities that are correlated with increased population growth. The marine resources of Point Loma are ecologically rich, scientifically interesting, and highly threatened.

THE MARINE SYSTEMS OF POINT LOMA

Point Loma is a peninsula and is therefore surrounded on three sides by water. Although made up of less than three square miles of land, the Point is bordered by seven miles of rocky, sandy, and developed shoreline. The western, ocean-facing portion of the coast is undeveloped rocky habitat, including areas under the jurisdiction of the National Park Service, the Navy, the Coast Guard, and the City of San Diego (Point Loma Wastewater Treatment Plant). The southern end of the Point, Cabrillo National Monument, is one of the best protected and easily accessible tidepool areas in southern California. Just offshore to the west is the largest and best-studied kelp forest on the West Coast, which covers up to four square miles. Farther offshore, but within view of land, is an important migratory pathway for Pacific gray whales (*Eschrichtius robustus*), which pass by every year on their way to calving grounds in Baja California, Mexico. The eastern coast of the peninsula faces San Diego Bay. It is characterized by a combination of rocky and sandy shoreline, but more than half of it is highly developed for various Navy and port operations. Although the soft-bottomed bay habitat is interesting (including some vulnerable seagrass beds), we will describe only the hard-bottomed communities. In addition, "Point Loma" here is defined as the southernmost, federally managed part of the peninsula.

The hard-bottomed communities include the rocky intertidal "tidepool" area and the kelp forest. The word "intertidal" refers to the area between high and low tides along the shore. Tidepools are depressions where water is trapped during low tides, forming small pools that provide habitat for numerous plants, invertebrates, and fish. These depressions are formed over geologic time through a combination of biological, physical, and chemical processes. First, a small pit in the rock is eroded by waves or by the burrowing of an animal, such as a chiton. After the animal has vacated its home, water is trapped in the burrow during low tide, and the respiration of the different plants and animals trapped in the water forms excess carbon dioxide. This carbon dioxide makes the water slightly acidic,

How tidepools are formed. At Point Loma the tidepools show varying stages of development.

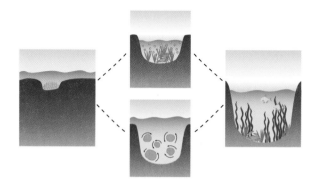

which slowly dissolves the rock a little more. Small cobbles get stuck in the pool, which get rolled around by the waves during high tide, eroding the rock further. Over thousands of years, the pool grows larger. The tidepools at Point Loma are in various stages of development, from the new burrows of chitons to large pools full of juvenile fish and lobsters. Although the whole rocky intertidal is often referred to as the "tidepool area," it is important to note that shelves and boulder fields surround the pools, and these also provide great habitat for the multitude of organisms that call this zone home.

"Kelps" are a class of brown algae that can grow to large sizes. They are attached to the bottom and may have flotation devices to buoy themselves toward the surface of the water. A number of species can be found in the intertidal, but far more impressive are the large forests of kelps that grow subtidally (beyond the intertidal, where the bottom is always submerged), in water about 25 to 70 feet deep. Much like terrestrial forests, these stands of plants are made up of various species. In Point Loma they are dominated by giant kelp (*Macrocystis pyrifera*). Giant kelp is aptly named, for it can grow up to 150 feet long as it forms a dense canopy after reaching the surface. The kelp itself provides habitat and food for many types of plants and animals.

Kelp forest and rocky intertidal communities are important both ecologically and economically. The kelp canopy (the upper 4 feet of the water column) is harvested for the production of alginates, used as a thickener and stabilizer in a wide variety of products including foods, pharmaceuticals, and cosmetics. On average, 20,000 tons of kelp are harvested yearly from Point

HARVESTING GIANT KELP

Giant kelp is harvested by large vessels that operate like sea-going versions of the wheat harvesters used by farmers. En route to the kelp bed, the harvester

looks and functions much like any large ship. Upon reaching its destination, however, it undergoes an amazing transformation. Large cutting racks—reciprocating blades mounted at the base of a conveyor system —are lowered from the stern into not more than four feet of water. Main engines are secured, and a bow propeller pushes the vessel, stern first, through the water.

Once the reciprocating blades have cut the kelp, vertically rotating, toothed rollers prevent loose fronds from floating away. Guided by the rollers, the fronds then move up the conveyor and into a large bin that takes up most of the harvester's length. Depending on the density of the kelp bed, up to 600 tons of kelp can be gathered in eight hours.

Giant kelp is especially suitable for commercial use because the surface canopy can be harvested several times a year without disturbing the submerged parts of the plant, where growth and reproduction occur. The surface canopy is continually regenerated by the rapid growth of young fronds. From the giant kelp is extracted algin, a unique substance found in the cell walls of the kelp. It is algin that accounts for kelp's extreme flexibility and lets the plant withstand the forces of surf and surge. Algin serves as a thickening, stabilizing, and smoothing agent in hundreds of products ranging from salad dressings to cosmetics, dental impression compounds to antacid formulations, canned foods to beer. It improves the texture and retains moisture in bakery products. In frozen foods, algin's stabilizing properties assure smooth texture and uniform thawing.

—Dale Glantz, ISP Alginates (formerly Kelco)

The surface canopy of Point Loma's offshore kelp forest.

Loma, with a value of $8 million. The most valuable commercial fisheries in the kelp forest are for red sea urchins (*Strongylocentrotus franciscanus*) and spiny lobsters (*Panulirus interruptus*); other valuable species taken include rock crabs (*Cancer* spp.) and fishes, such as the sheephead (*Semicossyphus pulcher*) and halibut (*Paralichthys californicus*). In the year 2000, landings were estimated at about $2.1 million. Casual, noncommercial harvesters do forage for some intertidal species elsewhere, but all harvesting is prohibited in Cabrillo National Monument.

Kelp forests are particularly appreciated for their high productivity and diversity. Observing the giant kelp forests on his voyage around the tip of South America, Charles Darwin wrote in 1834: *"I can only compare these great aquatic forests . . . with the terrestrial ones in the inter-tropical regions. Yet if in any country a forest was destroyed, I do not believe nearly so many species of animals would perish as would here, from the destruction of the kelp."*

Kelp forest communities harbor an amazing variety of organisms because of the high productivity of these algae, the number of microhabitats (specialized living spaces characterized by their physical or biological structure) they provide, and the frequent disturbances that prevent domination by only a few species. Holdfasts, the convoluted structures that anchor kelps to the bottom, shelter more than 150 species of invertebrates seeking hiding places, food, and living space. Other organisms live on the blades (analogous to leaves) and stipes (analogous to stems) of the kelp in different depths of the water column; some are associated with the surface canopy. Some other animals shelter or hunt near the kelps. The net result is that more than 800 species have been identified from kelp forest communities of southern California.

Although the kelp forest is a popular destination for recreational fishermen and scuba divers, the rocky intertidal provides an easily accessible and rewarding experience for visitors of all backgrounds. For many people, visiting the tidepools is the only direct experience they have with marine ecosystems. Cabrillo National Monument is an extremely popular destination for tourists, and it is estimated that more than 100,000 people visit the tidepools annually. Compared to sandy beaches, the diversity of life in the rocky intertidal is impressive. People go to the beach to swim, sunbathe, or surf, but they come to the tidepools to explore, experience, and learn.

ZONATION

To describe the basic natural history of the intertidal zone and tidepools, we first explore "zonation" in each system, and the combination of physical forces and biological adaptations that lead to this zonation. Looked at from above, intertidal animals and plants are patchily distributed; some areas are dominated by mussels, some by surfgrass, and some by other organisms. These various "zones" are much like the industrial, residential, and business districts of a city. Many classification systems have been developed for rocky intertidal areas, but here we will look at the zones most obvious on Point Loma.

Farthest inshore is the "splash zone," the part of the intertidal that is usually dry but is often splashed by larger waves. The "upper intertidal" is found just below the splash zone. This area is often submerged during higher high tides, but can also remain dry for a tidal cycle. On Point Loma, the splash and upper intertidal zones are mostly found on the sandstone cliffs

that border the tidepool area. Easily seen here are many small invertebrates such as periwinkle snails (*Littorina* spp.), lined shore crabs (*Pachygrapsus crassipes*), acorn barnacles (*Chthamalus* spp. and *Balanus glandula*), troglodyte chitons (*Nuttalina fluxa*), and various limpets. Little algae is found, except for small tufts of red and green algae and some encrusting forms often mistaken for rocks or tar.

Continuing down the shore, the "middle intertidal" tends to be fully submerged during high tide and fully exposed during low tide. Most of the available space is occupied in this zone, which contains several microhabitats. Beds of California mussels (*Mytilus californianus*) form an important habitat for a number of smaller organisms that live within the protection of the shells. Red algal turf is a group of seaweed species that form large mats covering much of the flat sections of the middle intertidal. Rockweed (*Silvetia fastigiata*) tends to grow in clumps on the tops and sides of boulders. Like mussel beds, turf and rockweed form important microhabitats for many other plants and animals.

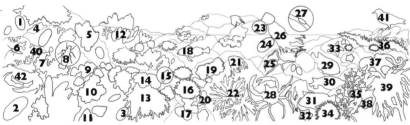

TIDEPOOL KEY

1. Coralline algae
2. Chiton
3. Limpet
4. Acorn barnacles
5. Goose neck barnacles
6. Rock louse
7. Sea lettuce
8. Kelp fly
9. Pink thatched barnacles
10. Encrusting algae
11. Periwinkles
12. Mussels
13. Dead man's fingers
14. Sea bubbles
15. Unicorn snail
16. Anemones
17. Tegula snails
18. Sculpin
19. Aggregating anemones
20. Sandcastle worms
21. Hermit crab
22. Rockweed
23. Wavy turban snails
24. Keyhole limpet
25. Brittle star
26. Surfgrass
27. Surfgrass limpet
28. Kelp crab
29. Garibaldi
30. Sea hare
31. Opaleye
32. Bat star
33. Knobby blue star
34. Urchin
35. Sargassum weed
36. Feather boa kelp
37. Octopus
38. Chestnut cowrie
39. Sea palm
40. Encrusting algae
41. Ruddy turnstone
42. Lined shore crab

KELP FOREST KEY

1. Harbor Seal
2. Norris' top snails
3. Bryozoan
4. Nudibranch
5. Bat stars
6. Kelp crab
7. Giant kelp
8. Rockfish
9. Scallops
10. Rockfish
11. Feather boa kelp
12. Kelp bass
13. Garibaldi
14. Pterygophora
15. Sheephead
16. Anchovies
17. Sea palm
18. Amphipod
19. Bryozoans
20. Wavy turban snail
21. Surf grass
22. Kelp holdfast
23. Brittle star
24. Sea urchin
25. California rock lobster
26. Abalone
27. Coralline algae
28. Chiton
29. Red algal turf

Farther offshore, the "lower intertidal" zone is often submerged during higher low tides and is never exposed during high tides. This area tends to be dominated by large patches of plants such as surfgrass (*Phyllospadix torreyi*) and kelps. In the tidepools of Point Loma, two kelps are common—the descriptively named feather boa kelp (*Egregia menziesii*), which grows to 15 feet, and the attractive southern sea palm (*Eisenia arborea*), which can grow 3 feet tall. Southern sea palms live exclusively in the very lowest part of the intertidal, which is exposed only during extreme low tides. These three plants are not restricted to the intertidal zone; they can be found growing as deep as 30 feet under water, or in the case of sea palms, to 100 feet. Very little space is unoccupied here—animals and plants live on, under, and within the grass and kelp beds.

Rockfish thrive in the kelp forest environs.

Farther into the subtidal is the kelp forest. Kelp forests are zoned by depth (surface to bottom), while the intertidal is zoned by tidal height (nearshore to offshore). The "canopy" of the forest is made up of giant kelp that grows to the surface, then stretches out horizontally. Closer to the bottom is an erect "understory," made up of kelps such as southern sea palms and *Pterygophora californica*, a multi-bladed kelp that grows to approximately 4 feet tall. Mixed in the understory are some prostrate kelps, such as the single-bladed *Laminaria farlowii*. Growing on the bottom are encrusting algae and algal turfs, much like in the intertidal. In addition, the kelp forest can often be interrupted by barren areas cleared of all kelp by sea urchins (*Strongylocentrotus* spp.) that attack attached plants when their normal food of drift algae is scarce.

Purple and red sea urchins' voracious grazing can place pressure on kelp communities.

Both the rocky intertidal and the kelp forest are dynamic systems subject to considerable disturbance over relatively short periods of time. Cliffs collapse, rocks are rolled, storms rip out kelps and mussels, water conditions fluctuate, and urchins can devour parts of the forest. Despite all these shifts on smaller scales, the zones remain intact when considered on larger scales. Zonation is caused by a number of physical and biological forces, and the various adaptations organisms have evolved to coexist with those forces. As these forces fluctuate in time and in space, so do the zones.

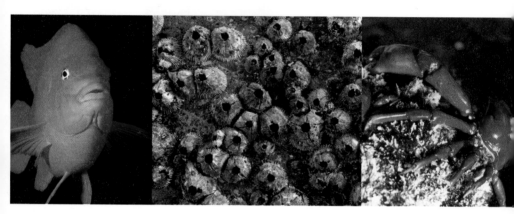

Some inhabitants of the rocky intertidal, left to right: young Garibaldi fish, barnacles at low tide, kelp crab, knobby seastar, California sea hare.

Why does zonation happen? All organisms face hardships in life—limited resources, physical stress, the danger of being eaten. Over millions of years, evolution allows organisms to adapt to these conditions to various degrees. However, adaptation is not a scripted or perfect process, and trade-offs often must be made. One organism might be able to take advantage of one set of conditions, but will fare poorly under others. Also, conditions are never static; disturbances can alter the distribution and abundance of animals on various scales. The outcome is a diverse array of species, fighting for survival with different degrees of success. These general principles are exemplified in the nearshore environments of Point Loma, with the ultimate result being the shifting mosaic of small-scale patches blended into the larger-scaled pattern mentioned above. In the next section, we will explore the various adaptations of organisms that lead to these patterns.

ROCKY INTERTIDAL Most rocky intertidal organisms evolved from marine ancestors and are adapting to semiterrestrial conditions. Twice a day the tide recedes, exposing all the creatures to air and direct sunlight, meaning they must protect themselves against desiccation (drying out), suffocation, and great temperature fluctuations. Different species do this in different ways. Aggregating anemones (*Anthopleura elegantissima*) will

pull their tentacles in and cover themselves with bits of shell and sand to stay moist. In addition, by living in crevices they can limit their exposure to sun and air. Limpets are flattened snails related to abalones. Casual observers often believe limpets are sessile creatures, but they are territorial grazers that move during high tide. During low tides when most people observe them, limpets clamp themselves tightly against the rocks to retain water under their shells. Other creatures do not try to fight against desiccation, but instead can cope with a certain amount of drying. The outer fronds (branches) of a rockweed "bush" will simply dry out during low tide and quickly rehydrate during high tide. The lower fronds remain wet, and many other plants and animals take advantage of this by living within them. Indeed, many of the microhabitats already mentioned—turf mats, mussel and anemone patches, seagrass beds, and the tidepools themselves—are often moist refuges for smaller creatures. Fishes, lobsters, and octopuses (*Octopus bimaculoides*), which must be underwater all the time, can live much higher in the intertidal by remaining in tidepools. For plants, different parts of the same rock can contain different microhabitats. For example, many plants grow on the shady sides of rocks out of direct sunlight.

As stressful as low tide can be, high tide does not bring much relief. Waves can deliver great bursts of energy that smash animals and roll rocks around. There are a number of strategies to minimize damage from wave action. Barnacles use brute force—they are sessile for their whole adult life, and attach to rocks with a glue so strong that it has attracted the interest of the biotech industry for its cementing properties. Chitons, which are behaviorally similar to limpets, use their mouthparts to grind away rock into a depression that fits their bodies perfectly, allowing them to avoid much of the direct impact of waves and projectiles. Feather boa kelp is flexible and diffuses wave impact. Sandcastle worms (*Phragmatopoma californica*) have yet another life-history adaptation for dealing with wave damage. They are social worms that form large aggregations of tubes by gluing grains of sand together. Not surprisingly, they are vulnerable to wave damage. When exposed to fatal wave stress, they quickly succumb but release their gametes into the water before they are destroyed. Thus, their offspring are able to take advantage of the newly opened space quickly and maintain it long enough to reproduce. They are rather like fire-adapted plants on land that move into burned areas, even though they are inferior competitors under normal conditions.

Rockweed grows in clumps on boulders in the rocky intertidal zone.

Space can be severely limited in the lower intertidal, and competition can lead to brutal interference. Often, plants and animals will use another organism as their substrate—it is common to find mussels and limpets with shells covered by other organisms. Different colonies of genetically identical anemones, if they come into contact with each other while they spread over the rock surface, will fight each other with tentacles called acrorhagi that are packed with stinging cells. Sharp lines of bare space mark the division of warring colonies. Many mobile grazers such as owl limpets (*Lottia gigantea*) defend territories that they clear of other grazers. During high tide they patrol their territories, using the front of their shells like a bulldozer to knock invaders off the substrate.

The microhabitat created by rockweed exposed at low tide provides a moist refuge for small creatures and plants.

All animals need food. Many sessile animals are filter feeders, depending on the incoming tide to bring tiny phytoplankton and zooplankton that they sieve out of the water. Other animals, such as California sea hares (*Aplysia californica*) graze on larger seaweeds and must be somewhat mobile. A number of predators feed in the intertidal, including predatory snails (especially unicorn snails, *Mexicanthina lugubris*), birds, lobsters, and octopuses. Many predators do not tolerate exposure to air, and therefore animals that live higher in the intertidal are protected from them during low tides.

Clearly, the rocky intertidal contains a suite of organisms with different strengths and weaknesses, different needs and tolerances. As mentioned, the sum result of various forces and processes, and adaptations to them, is the distribution of organisms in zones along the gradient from land to sea. For example, barnacles can tolerate long periods of desiccation and tremendous wave energy, and so can live higher in the intertidal. With their ability to cope with more difficult conditions, they experience reduced competition for space with algae and less risk of predation for much of the day.

KELP FORESTS As in the intertidal, zonation in the kelp forest can be attributed to the adaptations of organisms to the physical and biological forces around them. Many of the same forces—wave action, competition for space, and grazing—come into play. Sunlight, which can lead to desiccation in the intertidal, is an essential resource for kelps. All plants need light

The environment of the kelp beds at Point Loma is indeed very forest-like.

to photosynthesize, and taller kelps can shade the kelps below. Giant kelp has adaptations that make it a superior competitor for light: using floats called pneumatocysts, it buoys itself to the surface of the water to maximize exposure. Even though it lacks a vascular system, this kelp can translocate the products of photosynthesis down to the lower, shaded parts of the plant. The offshore distribution of kelp is ultimately limited by light—deeper than about 70 feet, it is simply too dark for the younger stages of giant kelp to get started.

Potentially, giant kelp could persist anywhere shallower than this light limit, and occasionally it does grow as far inshore as the intertidal. But generally it is not found in water shallower than 15 feet, because the force of breaking waves is too great. Giant kelps are well adapted for moderate stress from wave action; fronds are lost quite easily, although the structures that anchor the kelp to the bottom persist. The whole plant can live up to five years, but individual fronds only last four to six months. New fronds grow continuously and quickly (up to a foot a day) throughout the life of the kelp. Although these kelps can tolerate occasional wave damage, severe waves can dislodge the holdfast, which in turn tangles with and dislodges other kelps. The constant pounding of surf in shallower depths is too great for them to persist. Their morphology, which allows them to grow above other kelps in deeper water, also leaves them too vulnerable to waves to inhabit shallower waters.

Even if kelp loses some of its fronds, the holdfast can grow back as long as a few stipes remain.

The tension between growth toward the surface to take advantage of light and susceptibility to wave forces can be seen in understory kelps as well. Species with long stipes and short blades, such as *Pterygophora*, grow taller than the other understory plants and receive more light. Those with short stipes and long blades, such as *Laminaria*, tend to lie along the bottom, but are more flexible and are better able to resist wave damage. When water rushes past dense stands of kelp, the drag of the plants can dampen waves and slow currents. Darwin noted that just inshore of kelp forests, the water is "quiet." Although clumped plants will shade each other, they will also protect each other from wave action.

Kelps are very sensitive to low nutrients, and nutrient limitations often restrict the geographic distribution of giant kelp. Water temperature is highly correlated with nutrient levels;

warmer water tends to be poorer in essential nutrients for plant growth. Because temperature is such a good predictor of nutrient availability, it is also the best predictor of kelp growth. Kelps will not grow in water warmer than 68 degrees Fahrenheit. A number of other physical forces will affect the distribution of kelp forests, such as the type of bottom, the amount of sediment, and salinity.

HOW DO THE SYSTEMS INTERACT?

People visit the tidepools by foot during low tide, but must get in the water using scuba or snorkel gear to see the kelp forest. This separation in the way the two systems are experienced gives the false impression that they are isolated from each other. But the animals, plants, and the water itself are unaware of our classification system and don't respect such distinctions. As mentioned, surfgrass and some kelps can be found growing from the intertidal into the shallow parts of the kelp forest. Many animal species, such as purple urchins (*Strongylocentrotus purpuratus*), Kellet's whelks (*Kelletia kelletii*), and knobby stars (*Pisaster giganteus*) are found in both systems. Lobsters and opaleye (*Girella nigricans*) use the intertidal as a nursery, spending their youth in the tidepools and moving to the kelp forest as adults. The two systems are both affected by many of the same disturbances—large storms, changes in water temperature, and pollution.

In addition, the kelp forest is a source of food for the intertidal. Some of the dislodged fronds get swept out to sea, but a large portion of this material ends up in the intertidal. After a storm, the tidepools of Point Loma are often covered with pieces of giant kelp, which is consumed by urchins, sea hares, kelp flies, and microbes, the source of the strong sulfur smell visitors occasionally note.

Both systems are also part of the ocean at large. In fact, many adult animals that live in the tidepools or kelp forest have spent the early part of their lives farther offshore as microscopic larvae, unable to swim against the currents. The parents release the larvae nearshore and then they are carried away by the currents for hours to months, possibly transported great distances. Most of the larvae will perish through predation, starvation, or isolation. A few will get swept back to shore in the proper amount of time for them to metamorphose into settling juveniles or recruits. The adults at Point Loma could have parents that live hundreds of miles away. Giant kelps release spores, which spend only a few hours as plankton before settling; they disperse only a few yards during this phase. However, when adult kelps are ripped off the bottom they can still reproduce; if drifting kelps are carried to appropriate habitat, they are able to colonize. This is an alternate mechanism of dispersal for these kelps.

Giant kelp can become sickly during warm El Niño periods.

Variations in ocean climate affect both systems greatly and directly. El Niños, for example, have two important manifestations in southern California. First, winter storms are formed much farther south during El Niño years, leaving local coastlines more vulnerable without the shelter usually provided by the Channel Islands. Huge waves during the 1983 and 1998 El Niño events caused massive mortality of kelp plants and led to the collapse of sandstone cliffs and death of splash-zone organisms in the intertidal. The second effect is a decrease in essential nutrients in the water due to changes in ocean circulation. Starved of nutrients and exposed to increased wave stress, many giant kelp plants grow more slowly, or cease to grow. The surface canopy deteriorates, and in extreme cases the bases of the kelp plants die.

During an El Niño many of the ecological functions of kelps—such as providing habitat for young kelp bass (*Paralabrax*

Pelagic crabs come up from the south during El Niño.

clathratus) and food for sea urchins and abalones—are greatly reduced or eliminated. These conditions will affect other plants, such as intertidal seaweeds, in the same manner. El Niño events last from one to three years in California, and recovery is rapid once oceanographic conditions return to normal. The opposite phase of this atmospheric and oceanic oscillation, La Niña, is characterized by unusually cold, nutrient-rich conditions. Subtidal kelp and intertidal algal populations flourish during this phase of the cycle.

In addition to episodic El Niño and La Niña events, ocean climate also includes shifts on the scale of tens of years. Since 1977 the ocean has become warmer, and this has reduced the average size of kelp plants. If global warming has similar effects on the nearshore environment, it will lead to local reductions in the kelps and the resources they support, as well as the loss of species that cannot tolerate warmer waters.

THREATS TO THE SYSTEMS

The tidepools of Point Loma look quite different now than when Cabrillo and Vizcaíno first arrived. In recent decades, a number of studies have documented ecological changes in the region. Concerned about the effects of heavy visitation to Cabrillo National Monument's tidepool area, Joy Zedler and her students from San Diego State University studied human impacts in the area in 1976 and 1978. Since 1990, the National Park Service has been monitoring the rocky intertidal in three sites in the park, while the Navy and scientists from the University of California Santa Barbara monitor two sites farther north on the Point. These studies, combined with independent academic research and anecdotal information from park employees and visiting scientists, allow us to draw clear conclusions about population changes over time and make better educated policies to try to manage them. For example, a third of the park's intertidal was closed to visitors after results of five years of monitoring indicated that a number of species have experienced alarming declines.

Black abalone has not been seen on Point Loma since 1990.

Abalone, both black (*Haliotis cracherodii*) and green (*H. fulgens*), were once quite abundant but are now virtually gone from the area. Zedler found several black abalones in her studies, but not a single one has been documented on Point Loma since 1990. A combination of overharvesting and a bacterially induced epidemic has devastated these populations throughout southern California. Dave Leighton, who studied green abalone in the region, reported that they were extremely common on the southern end of the Point until the late 1960s. To slow the erosion of the land above, riprap was placed along the edge of the cliff. These granite boulders dramatically changed sedimentation patterns in the area, and the green abalone nursery ground was buried in sand. Occasionally a green abalone is found, but the population has not shown signs of significant recovery. Ochre sea stars (*Pisaster ochraceus*) were once common, but have since disappeared from the area; since 1990 a single individual has been documented. Curiously, these sea stars can be found in nearby tidepool areas in La Jolla, Ocean Beach, and Baja California. The cause of this local change is not known, but possible hypotheses include warming water temperatures, disease, and lack of food. The National Park Service monitoring program has detected an alarming decline in California mussels since 1990. The trend is interesting, since the area closed to visitors has been hit the hardest, going from approximately 50% mussel cover in 1990 to near 0% in 1999. Populations have been recovering in the most highly visited area, which increased from 10% mussel cover in 1990 to about 30% in 1999. Park staff are studying the cause of this trend; possible causes include pollution from the bay, increasing water temperatures, and a lack of new recruits.

A park ranger does a photo plot as a means of monitoring the tidepools.

Different areas of Point Loma intertidal experience different types of exploitation. A relatively small section of Cabrillo National Monument receives intense visitation, but enforcement of poaching rules is stringent. In contrast, the northern part of the Point, which is not within a national park, is hard to reach and receives few visitors, but collecting is more common. This difference is reflected in the sizes of owl limpets, which are occasionally poached as a substitute for abalone. Because poachers tend to take the largest animals, they can cause the average size of individuals in the population to be smaller. In the spring of 1995, for example, the average size of owl limpets at Navy sites in northern Point Loma was 1.4 inches, with the largest recorded animal at 2.5 inches. That same season, the average at Cabrillo was 1.7 inches, with the largest at 3.3 inches. This shift in size is particularly important since owl limpets change sex from male to female as they get larger. Poachers are selectively removing the larger females and could change the gender distribution and reduce the net reproduction of the population.

The extra level of protection afforded by the park comes with a cost. The mission statement of the National Park Service is both to conserve and "provide for the enjoyment" of our natural resources—accessibility to the park can often conflict with our desire to protect it. The high visitation area is concentrated in a 0.2-mile stretch of coastline. Human foot traffic has a big effect on the thickness and species composition of red algal turf habitat. The turf in the closed area is more than twice as thick as the highly visited area and is comprised of different species of algae. This difference is reflected in the invertebrate communities living in the turf. In the summer of 2000, there were six times more microscopic snails living in the thicker turf, and a greater diversity of invertebrates.

Before the federal Clean Water Act was passed, sewage pollution was a serious threat to kelp forests near major urban centers. Giant kelp literally went extinct on the Palos Verdes Peninsula, the site of the Los Angeles County discharge—the water became cloudy, light was blocked from reaching the plants, and the bottom was covered with silt, preventing settlement of new plants. The Point Loma kelp forest was also affected in the late 1950s and early 1960s, when a combination of sewage, intense sea-urchin grazing, and the 1957–1959 El Niño decimated local populations. In 1963, the Point Loma Wastewater Treatment Plant with a deepwater ocean outfall went on line. Once sewage was no longer being released nearshore and oceanographic conditions returned to normal, the

The kelp forest suffered greatly from the decline of sea otters and sheephead, both predators of destructive sea urchins.

kelp forest recovered. Today, with advanced primary treatment and sewage discharge in 300 feet of water four and a half miles offshore, there is no detectable effect on the kelp forest. Concern about coast pollution has shifted away from sewage disposal toward diffuse nonpoint sources, mainly runoff from land carrying oily discharges from automobiles, heavy metals, and toxic organic chemicals such as pesticides. Fortunately, Point Loma has a small watershed, much of which is not urbanized, and therefore little runoff reaches the marine environment. Yet, pollution problems may be associated with the flushing of San Diego Bay to the south and Mission Bay to the north, both of which have large urban watersheds.

A more serious threat to the integrity of kelp forest communities comes from poorly managed fisheries. As in owl limpet poaching, fishing selectively targets the largest members of exploited species, leading to decline in the average size of individuals in many marine populations. For instance, spiny lobsters taken in the 1880s were almost twice the size of the average spiny lobster harvested today. Because reproduction in many marine animals increases exponen-

tially with size, removal of the largest animals can lead to a dramatic decrease in reproductive capacity. Many species, such as abalone, release eggs and sperm into the water where they are fertilized externally. For abalone, males and females must be within about 6 feet of each other for fertilization to be successful. Fishing has eliminated the high densities of spawners that were near enough to one another to produce most of the next generation. Consequently, abalone populations are at risk. All commercial and recreational harvesting of abalone south of San Francisco has been banned since 1997. One species, the white abalone (*Haliotis sorenseni*), was placed on the endangered species list in 2001, while the black abalone was added to the "candidate list" for endangered species protection in 1999.

Hungry sea urchins can eliminate large areas of kelp, so anything that affects their abundance can have far-reaching ramifications. Before humans inhabited the San Diego region, sea otters (*Enhydra lutris*) preyed on sea urchins and probably controlled their populations. Native Americans hunted otters for food, and later Russians and Europeans coveted otters for their thick pelts. Due to exploitation, sea otters were probably absent from southern California by the early 1800s. Two other predators, spiny lobsters and sheephead, were important urchin consumers until their populations were greatly reduced by fisheries in the mid-1900s. Abalones are competitors of sea urchins, since they share the same food and space requirements. And, as already noted, abalone populations have seen extreme declines in the past few decades; large-scale abalone fisheries began in 1850, and modern abalone fisheries greatly reduced populations by the late 1960s. With reduced competition for food and space, and with less pressure from predators, sea urchin populations exploded in the 1950s and 1960s. Hordes of them were observed eating kelp plants.

In the early 1970s a fishery was developed for sea urchins, whose roe is exported to Japan as a delicacy. This new fishery helped control urchin populations and grazing pressure in kelp communities. But only the larger red sea urchin is being fished; purple sea urchins, which are also capable of destructive grazing, are too small to process economically. If intense fishing pressure on urchin predators continues, urchin barrens will become increasingly common. Thus, fisheries for just a few species can lead to increased urchin abundances, widespread

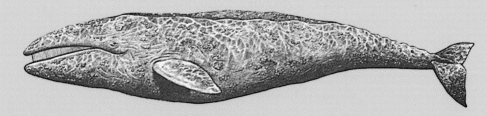

GRAY WHALES

By far the largest mammals in the Point Loma area are the Pacific gray whales, which pass by on epic annual migrations between December and March. At 45 feet long and 33 tons, these impressive marine mammals spend summers feeding in the cool, northern waters of the Chukchi and Bering seas. In early autumn, gray whales head south along the west coast for Mexico, a 5,000-mile trip one way, the longest migration of any mammal on Earth.

First out are the pregnant females, followed by males and young. They stay within six miles of shore as they travel, passing within sight of Point Loma. The whales can remain underwater for as long as 15 minutes; when they surface, they exhale through two blowholes, sending up spouts of water and air that can be seen by observers on shore. Pregnant females will give birth during the journey, or soon after they arrive at one of a handful of lagoons in Baja California where they spend the winter. Nonpregnant females may mate enroute or in the lagoons, but their young will not be born until the following winter.

New calves average 15 feet in length and weigh about a ton. While in the calving lagoon, they nurse on their mother's milk, which is more than 50% fat. The calves grow quickly, gaining about a thousand pounds before starting the return trip north; they continue to feed on mother's milk as they move.

For forty to sixty years, a gray whale will continue this pattern. This predictability made them easy targets for hunters, who harvested the animals nearly to extinction in the nineteenth century. Gray whales have been protected from exploitation by the International Whaling Commission since 1946. They have made a remarkable comeback, and current populations are considered close to their estimated pre-exploitation numbers.

kelp mortality, and the loss of habitat and food for many other organisms, many of which are also commercially important. This strongly demonstrates the need for an ecosystem approach to fisheries management, which takes into account the effects of fishing on the target species as well as the effects on the community as a whole.

CONSERVATION EFFORTS To protect the natural marine resources of Point Loma, we must know what they are and how they are doing. This is done through extensive inventories and long-term ecological monitoring. As mentioned, the Point Loma rocky intertidal has been monitored by various entities, and the kelp forest has been studied since the 1950s and monitored consistently by researchers from Scripps Institution of Oceanography since 1971. These long-term observations, along with experimental research, allow scientists to separate the effects of some human-induced problems from natural disturbances. For example, in 1992 the Point Loma sewage outfall ruptured, affecting both the intertidal and the kelp forest. Long-term observations indicated that this two-month episode had minor impacts on the natural ecosystems with no long-lasting effects detected.

Other important conservation issues require more than long-term observations to understand and potentially solve; active management is necessary. Marine reserves, areas that are protected from human exploitation, can protect parent populations that produce the next generation. In addition, they can maintain ecosystems in a healthy state, with normal structure, function, and biodiversity. Reserves provide educational and recreational opportunities, and can serve as vital control sites for scientific studies. The tidepools in Cabrillo National Monument are a well-protected marine reserve, but they are part of a larger nearshore system. They depend on larvae from elsewhere to sustain their populations, but most intertidal regions and subtidal areas in southern California are subject to heavy human use. Networks of well-designed marine reserves will be necessary for the long-term conservation of the Point Loma rocky intertidal and kelp forest. The future of marine resources in all of southern California may depend on our willingness to extend these protections to larger areas.

REFERENCES/ADDITIONAL READING

McPeak, Ronald H., Dale A Glantz, and Carole R. Shaw. 1988. *The Amber Forest: Beauty and Biology of California's Submarine Forests.* Watersport Publishing, San Diego. 144 pp. A beautiful, informative book that provides additional information about kelp forests. Kelp life history, inhabitants, and harvest are detailed with impressive graphics.

Ricketts, Edward F., Jack Calvin, and Joel W. Hedgpeth. 1985. *Between Pacific Tides.* Fifth edition. Stanford University Press, Palo Alto. 652 pp. The classic text for casual and expert tidepoolers alike. Not meant as a classic field guide, but explains basic intertidal ecology and describes many common intertidal species, including natural history information.

Brandon, Jeffrey L. and Frank Rokop. 1985. *Life Between the Tides.* American Southwest Publishing, San Diego. 228 pp. A small paperback useful for identifying intertidal animals in the field. The pictures are large and clear. Focuses specifically on organisms found in San Diego County.

Gotshall, Daniel W. 1994. *Guide to Marine Invertebrates: Alaska to Baja California.* Sea Challengers, Monterey, CA. 112 pp. A great softcover field guide for local subtidal invertebrates. Clear, interesting pictures. Publisher has a number of more specific field guides, most of which are colorful and useful. (Website: www.seachallengers.com). Check out "Pacific Coast Nudibranchs" to see some of the most beautiful creatures on Earth.

Morris, Robert H., Donald P. Abbott, and Eugene C. Haderlie. 1992. *Intertidal Invertebrates of California.* Stanford University

Press, Palo Alto. 670 pp. A large, comprehensive book, extremely useful for identifying more obscure animals, including many that range into the shallow subtidal.

Stewart, Joan G. 1991. *Marine Algae and Seagrasses of San Diego County.* California Sea Grant College, La Jolla. 197 pp. A smaller paperback that describes the many marine plants in the area. Illustrations only, no photographs, so more difficult for beginners. Still, very detailed and one of the best resources for learning about local algae.

A Mediterranean Place: Plant Communities

S tand at any high point in the Point Loma Ecological Reserve and you can see, and inhale the spicy aroma of, one of the rarest kinds of vegetation in the world. This is vegetation adapted to a Mediterranean climate of warm, dry spring, summer, and fall weather interrupted by a brief rainy season during cool winter months. Mediterranean climate occurs in only five places around the globe, on the west sides of continents where cold ocean currents meet warm land. These areas are widely separated—the Mediterranean Ocean basin in Europe, coastal California in the United States, southwestern coastal Chile, the tip of South Africa, and the south and southwest coasts of Australia. Only about 2% of the world's terrestrial vegetation is Mediterranean, and about 10% of that total occurs in California. Point Loma hosts a truly rare plant world.

Mediterranean vegetation looks—and smells—similar wherever it is found. Yet, Mediterranean plants from each continent are largely unrelated to one another. Instead, they have come to look alike through evolutionary adaptation to the peculiar demands of the climate. Through a process called convergent evolution, the plants in each area have developed similar solutions to the feast-or-famine rainfall patterns. They face the challenge of living most of the year without rainfall, but they are able quickly to mobilize resources and take advantage of water when it does come. We have the unique opportunity to see, feel, and smell some of those adaptations from the viewpoints and along the trails at Cabrillo National Monument and in the Point Loma Ecological Reserve.

AUTHOR

Dr. Kathryn McEachern is a plant ecologist with the U.S. Geological Survey-BRD, Channel Islands Field Station. Her research interests include rare plant population monitoring and plant community analysis.

PLANT ADAPTATIONS

Mediterranean plants have evolved several basic adaptations to take advantage of winter rain and yet survive summer drought. Many trees and shrubs have thick, waxy evergreen leaves designed to conserve water. With their tough, spiny leaves, these plants sometimes are called "hard chaparral" species. They manage to stay green and productive all summer by growing very slowly, using specialized metabolic processes that conserve water.

Some shrubs display another common adaptation—they are drought-deciduous. They produce leaves quickly when it rains but lose them when the soils dry out. It is not unusual for some of these plants to produce and discard several sets of leaves a year when winter rain is interrupted by even relatively brief dry spells. Because their leaves are soft and often downy, these plants are sometimes called "soft chaparral" shrubs. These plants stay productive over the course of a year by mobilizing forces to grow quickly when water is available, and shutting down to a near dormant state when it is dry. Southern Californians often comment on how rapidly the vegetation turns green and fragrant with the beginning of seasonal rains. They are observing the rapid transfer of chlorophyll and other compounds to new leaves in the drought-deciduous vegetation.

Dudleya
(*Dudleya lanceolata*)

A third strategy seen in both woody shrubs and herbaceous perennials is the use of one or more organs, such as leaves, stems, or roots, for water storage. In fact, the proportion of stem and leaf succulent plants in the Mediterranean plant communities increases toward the equator on each continent. Point Loma is near the northern limit in California for many such succulents. The vegetation here displays a unique mixing of northern and south-

ern species, giving Point Loma some of the highest species
diversity among any coastal California vegetation.

The leaves of many Mediterranean plants are spe-
cially designed to minimize water loss. Many of
the Point Loma plants have light-colored woolly
or hairy leaves, or leaves that are held vertically,
which helps reflect sunlight and shade the leaf
surface. Leaf cross sections show that the stoma-
tal pores, used to exchange carbon dioxide and
other gases necessary for photosynthesis, are located in pits sunken below the surface or on the shaded
undersides of leaves. This adaptation reduces passive water
loss through the pores. Another less visible adaptation occurs
in the root systems. Many perennials develop long taproots to
reach water stored deep in the soil for seedling growth. Later
the plants produce fine, shallow roots close to the surface that
can absorb rainwater before it runs off of steep slopes. These
roots can be dormant or active as the need arises.

Lemonadeberry (*Rhus integrifolia*)

Finally, plants with an annual life history avoid drought
altogether. They germinate from seed, grow, flower, produce
seeds, and die during the rainy season. They are present for
most of the year as
seeds lying dormant in
the soil—an important
component of the veg-
etation often
overlooked
and largely
unknown
by visitors in
the dry season.
Together with the
drought-deciduous
species, annuals contrib-
ute to the spectacular spring

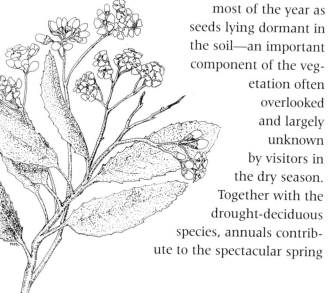

Toyon (*Heteromeles arbutifolia*)

TABLE I : PLANT ADAPTATIONS TO MEDITERRANEAN CLIMATE

MEDITERRANEAN CLIMATE ADAPTATION	POINT LOMA EXAMPLE
Thick, waxy evergreen leaves	Wart-stemmed ceanothus (*Ceanothus verrucosus*)
Drought-deciduous leaves	California sagebrush (*Artemisia californica*)
Succulent stems, leaves or roots	Cliff spurge (*Euphorbia misera*)
Sunken stomatal pores	Toyon (*Heteromeles arbutifolia*)
Pores on leaf undersides	Mission manzanita (*Xylococcus bicolor*)
Woolly or downy leaves	Black sage (*Salvia mellifera*)
Leaves held vertically	Lemonadeberry (*Rhus integrifolia*)
Taproot and shallow surface roots	Chamise (*Adenostoma fasciculatum*)
Annual life history	Fiddleneck (*Amsinckia menziesii*)

beauty of the Mediterranean vegetation—the snowy white, diminutive cryptantha (*Cryptantha intermedia*) and the purple nightshade (*Solanum xanti*), for example.

These adaptations can be seen in Mediterranean plants all around the globe. Most use a combination of traits in their unique solutions to the challenge of survival through repeated wet and dry cycles. As a result, the global Mediterranean vegetation types display high biodiversity, even though they have all converged on common solutions to the Mediterranean climate challenge.

WHY SO FRAGRANT, AND WHAT ARE THE SIDE EFFECTS?

A striking characteristic of Mediterranean vegetation is the spicy aroma. Why does the vegetation smell so? Compared to plants in less stressful climates, these grow slowly. For them, leaves are "expensive," because the plant must spend a large portion of its annual energy budget to make a leaf. Whether the strategy is to make fewer, tough evergreen leaves or many throw-away, soft, deciduous leaves, the plant can't afford to lose them to grazing animals. Therefore the leaves contain oily, aromatic compounds that are distasteful to insects and other herbivores. Often plants have thorns and spines for added protection.

These chemical compounds can be useful, or poisonous. Many culinary spices come from plants in Mediterranean areas of the world. On the other hand, the oils in some species, like poison oak (*Toxicodendron diversilobum*) or spice bush (*Cneoridium dumosum*), cause skin rashes in people. Compounds in the pollen of others, like California sagebrush (*Artemisia californica*), give people hay fever during the flowering season.

PLANTS AND FIRE

A side effect of this strategy to deter grazers with fragrant oils is that the aromatic compounds are flammable. In modern California, fire typically returns to the same place every 20 to 30 years. Before settlement and urbanization, the fire-return frequency was most likely 80 to 100 or more years, depending upon geographic location. As with many complex systems, one solution begets another challenge. The secondary challenge for chaparral plants is to survive where fire is a part of the system. Not surprisingly, Mediterranean plants throughout the world have adjusted their life cycles to fire. Again, this is an evolutionary response to an environmental situation, even though this situation is brought on in part by the plants themselves.

California sagebrush (*Artemisia californica*)

Most chaparral plants can be put into one of three categories, depending upon how they respond to wildfire. "Sprouters" grow back from fire-resistant stem or root tissue that forms at, or just under, ground level as the plant grows. This tissue, called

The vegetation at Point Loma has adapted to a Mediterranean climate— a climate found only in four other places on earth.

a "burl," looks like a swollen part of the stem. Sprouters that have been burned have several stems coming from the burl, and often there are traces of charred wood on the burl. The bigger the burl, the more resources a plant has to resprout vigorously after fire. The root systems and burls of these plants can be very old. Some are known to have survived several fires 100 or more years apart. Once the burl is destroyed, the plant dies. Then, the species has to rely upon seed to repopulate the area—a most uncommon occurrence for most sprouters.

"Seeders" produce new plants from seed after fire. They produce seed crops every year, and the seeds accumulate and remain dormant in the soil in a "seed bank." When fire occurs, the heat and chemicals in smoke and ash are needed to cause the seed embryo to break dormancy and produce a new plant. Seeds of these plants can stay dormant for astonishingly long periods of time. Some more than a hundred years old have been germinated from herbarium specimens. To make things more interesting, the sprouter and seeder fire strategies are found in both the hard and soft chaparral plant types.

Finally, there is a large group of annual plants that sprout after fire and live out their life cycle in that same year. These "fire followers" produce some of the most spectacular flower displays in the world. They produce a flush of seeds and are not seen again until after the next fire. These species also have enormous seed longevity. Collectively, the annuals are probably the most complex and diverse group of species in Mediterranean vegetation. Some annuals germinate after rainfall, others appear after fire, while still others require both fire and rain. Through the years many different annual species will be seen in the same area, depending upon which environmental cues have selected them to appear from the soil seed bank.

Buckthorn is a "seeder" producing new plants from seeds after a fire.

Standing on that high point and looking out over Point Loma, it is fascinating to imagine the diverse challenges that brought this native vegetation together. These plants are solving the simultaneous problems of getting water when it is available, persisting and growing in the face of annual drought, avoiding herbivory, and exploiting occasional fires for renewed population growth. Cabrillo National Monument at Point Loma is one of the few protected places in the world where this convergence of factors can be fully appreciated.

PLANT COMMUNITIES

When we talk about plant adaptations, we are referring to effects of natural selection over thousands of years in individual species. When we look at a landscape, we notice that some species tend to group together. This is because they have similar

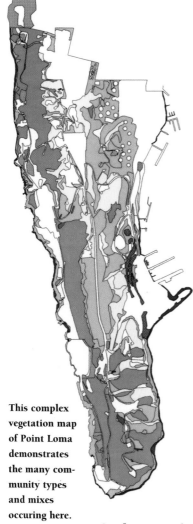

This complex vegetation map of Point Loma demonstrates the many community types and mixes occuring here.

requirements for sun or shade, temperature and relative humidity, fog deposition or dryness. Perhaps they do best on similar kinds of soil, or they respond to certain types of disturbances like wind or salt spray in a similar fashion. Or, perhaps they simply need to avoid the competition of other plants, even though they would grow just fine in the habitats of those competitors. For a multitude of reasons, species tend to group together in predictable ways on the landscape. These groups of ecologically similar species are called plant communities.

Showing the boundaries of a plant community can be a tricky job. Usually one community grades into another, so that there is a zone of mixing between them. But community groupings are given validity by data collected at many places over many years by many different scientists. Plant communities are usually described by listing the most common, or dominant, species first, followed by the less common, and even temporally rare, species. Often the structure of the community is described, for example—whether the vegetation is tall and shrubby, or patchy with lots of open ground. In fact, we find that large-scale communities, with smaller-scaled local variation, occur consistently throughout California. So, for example, California chaparral extends from the northern Sierran foothills into the low mountains of Baja California, in Mexico. Similarly, coastal sage scrub is a community that occurs intermittently in a narrow band along the coast from Big Sur into northern Baja California. Local variations on these basic themes exist because each place is unique. The challenge for scientists and land managers is to understand the complexity of plant communities in their local landscapes, so that they can manage for the common while preserving the unique.

POINT LOMA PLANT COMMUNITIES Approximately half the acreage of the Federal Reservation on Point Loma is developed, and the land at the base of the peninsula is totally urban. Developments on the Point include facilities and roads, landscaped areas, and weedy sites where native plants have been removed and the soil has been disturbed. These developments are concentrated on the flattest areas of the Point, occupying nearly all the ridgeline and the marine terraces along the ocean and San Diego Bay. As a consequence, native vegetation is found mainly on the steep slopes. A few small buildings or weapons stations were located within intact native vegetation, but much of the native vegetation still occurs in fairly large, contiguous parcels. The less internal fragmentation there is, the better for conservation, and so the native vegetation that remains at Point Loma is of relatively high quality.

ARE TORREY PINES NATIVE TO POINT LOMA?

People often ask whether the Torrey pines (*Pinus torreyana*) near the lighthouse are native to Point Loma. These trees were planted in the mid-1930s, and they are doing quite well. A few saplings have been seen, apparently coming from seeds of planted trees. We don't know for sure whether Torrey pines grew naturally on Point Loma in historic times. They were widespread in the southwestern United States when the weather was cooler and moister, about 35 to 50 million years ago. Now they are extremely rare in nature, occuring in only two native populations. One is called Torrey Pines State Reserve north of San Diego, and the other is on Santa Rosa Island, California.

Four natural plant communities exist on Point Loma, recognized through mapping and sampling, and by comparing them to similar plant communities throughout California and Baja. They are coastal sage succulent scrub, southern maritime chaparral,

TABLE 2: PLANT COMMUNITIES OF POINT LOMA

PLANT COMMUNITY	COMMON OR DIAGNOSTIC PLANTS	ECOLOGICAL ADAPTATIONS	COMMUNITY CHARACTERISTICS
Coastal sage succulent scrub	*Artemisia californica*	Dd Sprouter	
	Salvia mellifera	Dd Sprouter	Low-growing vegetation
	Eriogonum fasciculatum	Dd Sprouter	with bluish-green color,
	Encelia californica	Dd Sprouter	1-5 feet tall, canopy cover
	Rhus integrifolia	Ev Sprouter	60-100%. Densest stands
	Euphorbia misera	Ev/Lf Su Seeder	on east-facing (bayside)
	Opuntia littoralis	Ev St Su Seeder	slopes, more open on
	Dudleya lanceolata	Ev Lf Su Seeder	upper oceanward slopes.
	Dudleya edulis	Ev Lf Su Seeder	
Southern maritime chaparral	*Ceanothus verrucosus*	Ev Seeder	Dense stands of dark green
	Heteromeles arbutifolia	Ev Sprouter	vegetation, 6-12 feet tall,
	Malosma laurina	Ev Sprouter	canopy cover usually 100%.
	Xylococcus bicolor	Ev Sprouter	Most dense in ravines,
	Quercus dumosa	Ev Sprouter	sometimes extending up
	Adenostoma fasciculatum	Dd Seeder & Sprouter	onto north-facing ridges. Most common bayside.
Southern coastal bluff scrub	*Lycium californicum*	Dd Sprouter	Fine textured, medium
	Suaeda californica	Dd Seeder	green vegetation 3 feet tall
	Distichlis spicata	Grass	at coastal bluff edges, in
	Isocoma menziesii	Ev Sprouter	narrow bands several feet wide and up to 100 feet long. Canopy cover 80-100%
Southern foredune scrub	*Abronia maritima*	Herb	Herbaceous community
	Camissonia cheiranthifolia	Herb	occupying low dunes immediately inland from
	Ambrosia bipinnatifida	Herb	beaches.

Dd – Drought-deciduous, Ev – Evergreen, St Su – Stem succulent, Lf Su – Leaf succulent. See text for discussion of adaptations.

coastal bluff scrub, and foredune scrub. Collectively, vegetation dominated by shrubs is called "scrub." As can be seen from the names, the Point Loma plant communities generally are all dominated by shrubs, but in different species combinations. Table 2 lists the most common plants and some distinguishing structural characteristics of each plant community.

Coastal Sage Succulent Scrub and Southern Maritime Chaparral The two most widespread natural plant communities of Point Loma, making up about 45% of the land cover, are coastal sage succulent scrub and southern maritime chaparral. They are easy to distinguish from one another, particularly in the summer. Coastal sage succulent scrub is composed mainly of drought-deciduous soft chaparral species, with a fair number of succulent herbs and cacti in the driest sites. Southern maritime chaparral supports mainly evergreen, hard chaparral plants. The two communities are distributed across the landscape in a patchwork pattern.

The Point Loma peninsula lies entirely within a larger belt of coastal sage scrub that once formed a nearly continuous band several miles wide along the California coast from the Big Sur coast to northern Baja California near Rosario, Mexico. Coastal sage scrub used to occupy nearly two million acres in California. It constituted about 2.5% of the state's native vegetation before European settlement. It has been reduced to about 10% to 15% of its former acreage by agricultural and urban development. California sagebrush is a dominant species in the community throughout that north-south range, giving the coastal sage scrub its name.

California buckwheat is one of the indicator species for the coastal sage succulent community.

Geographically, Point Loma is situated where several succulent shrubs from Baja California reach their northern limits. But because of its cooler maritime climate, many of the more northerly shrubs are also found. As a result, Point Loma supports coastal sage succulent scrub with an unusual combination of northern and southern elements. Mixed with northern coastal sage scrub species are plants that inhabit Diegan coastal sage scrub from more inland areas of San Diego County, as well as elements of Vizcainan and Martirian coastal sage scrub from areas of coastal and montane Baja California.

Point Loma plant communities, left to right: coastal sage succulent scrub, maritime chaparral on right bank, foredune scrub, coastal bluff scrub.

Coastal sage succulent scrub occurs mainly in the driest locations on Point Loma. It is the most widespread native community, making up about two-thirds of the native vegetation remaining on the Point. It is found on slopes with southern exposures where the sun's rays are strongest, high on slopes where winds are strongest, and in places with thin or sandy, well-drained soils. It is particularly prevalent at the tip of Point Loma in Cabrillo National Monument, and along the more exposed and arid west side of the peninsula. But while California sagebrush is important, it does not totally dominate this community. Instead it is mixed in varying proportions with black sage (*Salvia mellifera*), California buckwheat (*Eriogonum fasciculatum*), California encelia (*Encelia californica*), and cliff spurge (*Euphorbia misera*). These species are all 2 feet to 5 feet

tall. The community can be quite dense on the east-facing, leeward side of the peninsula, where the shrub canopies touch to
form nearly total cover. The vegetation has a more open aspect
in drier sites, ranging from 60% to 90% cover.

In a few places, lemonadeberry (*Rhus integrifolia*) has
crowded out other coastal sage species. This shrub forms nearly
impenetrable thickets along the toes of some of the western,
oceanward slopes, particularly in Cabrillo National Monument.
This plant is a vigorous resprouter. It has been known to

increase slowly but steadily in moist pockets within coastal sage
vegetation in a few other places, even without fire to stimulate
sprouting. Its high density near the tip of Point Loma indicates
that there has been a long fire-free interval relative to other
sites in San Diego County.

Small, open patches exist that have a high local abundance of cacti and other succulents in a few of the driest places
within the coastal sage succulent scrub. These patches are less
than an acre in size, usually on sandstone outcrops high on
the southern and western slopes of the point. San Diego barrel cactus (*Ferocactus viridescens*), fish-hook cactus (*Mammalaria
dioica*), coastal cholla (*Opuntia prolifera*), golden-spined cereus
(*Bergerocactus emoryi*), and several live-forever species (*Dudleya
lanceolata, D. edulis*) can be found in these sites. The occurrence

of even these small patches, typical of areas much farther south, gives Point Loma higher overall biodiversity than areas only slightly farther north.

California chaparral is the most common plant community of the foothills and low mountains of southern California. Typically a more inland community than coastal sage scrub, it does make incursions into coastal sage scrub all along the California coast. Southern maritime chaparral is a geographically restricted coastal form of the much more widespread California chaparral community. On Point Loma, the dominant plant is wart-stemmed ceanothus (*Ceanothus verrucosus*), an evergreen shrub with a geographic distribution limited to coastal San Diego County and northern Baja California. Urban development covers much of the area historically inhabited by wart-stemmed ceanothus, which is now listed as threatened by the State of California.

Southern maritime chaparral is found on Point Loma in sheltered ravines where soils are deeper than on the uplands. It has nearly total canopy closure, forming dense thickets 6 to 12 feet tall wherever it occurs on Point Loma. The most extensive, tallest, and densest stands are on the east-facing, leeward slopes of the Point. Species that occur with wart-stemmed ceanothus include toyon (*Heteromeles arbutifolia*), chamise (*Adenostoma fasciculatum*), mission manzanita (*Xylococcus bicolor*), and coastal scrub oak (*Quercus dumosa*). These are all shrubs or small trees that occur as individuals or small clumps within or near the more extensive ceanothus canopy cover. Southern maritime chaparral totals about one-third of the native plant cover in the reserve.

Southern Foredune Scrub and Southern Coastal Bluff Scrub

Southern California foredune scrub and southern California coastal bluff scrub are the two remaining Point Loma plant communities. Both occupy isolated sites along the ocean and are dominated by plants tolerant of sandy soil and salt spray.

Foredune scrub occupies the low, relatively transient dunes that form at the inland edge of the beach, with a sparse herbaceous cover of beach evening primrose (*Camissonia cheiranthifolia*), beach burrweed (*Ambrosia chamissonis*), and sand verbena (*Abronia maritima*). There are only about 2 acres of foredune scrub at Point Loma, occurring at several small pocket beaches along the ocean shore. In other coastal areas, low shrubs also inhabit the community, but the Point Loma dunes are too small and incipient for shrub growth. Foredune scrub once occurred on beaches along the southern California coast from Point Conception into Baja California. Most has been lost to development, and now only disturbed and fragmented remnants appear throughout this community's former area.

Beach evening primrose in foredunes.

    Coastal bluff scrub is found where ocean bluffs are capped with a thin layer of sand blown from the cliff face. Like foredune scrub, this was once a more common community in southern California that has been reduced to remnants by urban development. There are about 40 acres of southern coastal bluff scrub on Point Loma. Various prostrate, salt-tolerant shrubs occupy the community throughout California. Boxthorn (*Lycium californicum*), goldenbush (*Isocoma menziesii*), sea blight (*Suaeda californica*), and saltgrass (*Distichlis spicata*) dominate coastal bluff scrub at Point Loma. Unlike areas farther north, cliff spurge and several other succulents more common farther south also enter the community, giving it added local diversity.

COMMUNITY ENDANGERMENT

Point Loma's plant communities are, not surprisingly, globally rare. But they are also ranked as extremely endangered or sensitive within California (Table 3). This status is the direct result of land development for agricultural and urban uses. Mediterranean coastal areas are among the most heavily developed places in the world. Coastal California follows only the European Mediterranean Basin in acres of native Mediterranean scrub lost to other uses.

A plant community rank as California endangered or extremely endangered means that the state must be consulted before development or invasive management action can be taken.

TABLE 3: ENDANGERMENT STATUS OF POINT LOMA PLANT COMMUNITIES

PLANT COMMUNITY	GLOBAL RANK	CALIFORNIA STATE RANK
Coastal sage succulent scrub	Extremely Endangered	Extremely Endangered
Southern maritime chaparral	Not Listed	Sensitive
Southern coastal bluff scrub	Extremely Endangered	Extremely Endangered
Southern foredune scrub	Endangered	Extremely Endangered

Note: The California Natural Diversity Database, maintained by the State of California Department of Game and Fish, rates California plant communities for protection according to their acreage and condition within the state and worldwide.

Further, because Point Loma has habitats used by birds listed under the Endangered Species Act, the U.S. Fish and Wildlife Service must also be involved in management planning.

The Point Loma Ecological Reserve is one of the few places in the world where these plant communities are managed for their own conservation. Even here they are at risk of further degradation through the invasion of nonnative plants, air and water pollution, habitat fragmentation, and edge effects. All these factors can lead to declines in biodiversity and community health. Managing such small remnants of ecosystems that evolved to function within much larger natural systems poses special challenges.

RARE PLANTS

Sixteen plant species listed as rare or sensitive by the California Natural Diversity Database occur on Point Loma, but only one, Orcutt's spineflower (*Chorizanthe orcut-tiana*), has legal protection because of its listing as endangered under the federal Endangered Species Act. This small annual plant is restricted to sandy soils in San Diego County, historically scattered from Point Loma north to near Encinitas, habitat that is now heavily developed. Orcutt's spineflower was thought to be extinct until new populations were found on Point Loma. Searches for more plants continue, and the plant and its habitat are protected from further disturbance.

Shaw's agave and sea dahlia are rare southern California plants.

A plant can be rare in several ways. Some species, like the spineflower, require habitats that occur only rarely in nature. They have high extinction risks because loss of only a few populations means a disproportionately large loss for the species. Others have distributions limited to habitats that are highly prized for development, and they become rare through loss of habitats. Eight Point Loma plants are in this category, including wart-stemmed ceanothus, coast woolly-heads (*Nemacaulis denudata* var. *denudata*), small-flowered microseris (*Microseris douglasii* ssp. *platycarpha*), Nuttall's lotus (*Lotus nuttallianus*), aphanisma (*Aphanisma blitoides*), short-lobed broomrape (*Orobanche parishii* ssp. *brachyloba*), coast wall flower (*Erysimum ammophilum*), and coastal scrub oak. Still others are rare in southern California, but they are more common farther south along the Baja California coast. Seven of the southern plants that give Point Loma its unusually high species diversity are in this category: Shaw's agave (*Agave shawii*), golden-spined cereus, sea dahlia (*Coreopsis maritima*), cliff spurge, San Diego barrel cactus, snake cholla, and San Diego sunflower (*Viguiera laciniata*).

VEGETATION HISTORY

Point Loma is one of the most striking geographic features of the southern California shoreline. The once-marshy terrain at the base of the peninsula and steep topography afforded some natural protection from the wood cutting, livestock grazing, and frequent fires that accompanied Native American and European settlement in the San Diego area. A strategic location at the mouth of San Diego Bay gave Point Loma added protection during a time of rapid twentieth-century urban development in California. The peninsula was used as a military base, and native vegetation was kept intact to camouflage defensive emplacements during the two world wars. So, by accident of natural geography, Point Loma supports one of the largest unfragmented stands of native vegetation on the southern

California coast today. In fact, much of the vegetation could be called "old growth"—a term usually applied to forests that have been undisturbed for about a century but that also applies to these largely shrub communities. Old growth stands are rare for any North American vegetation type. Those that do exist are considered treasures for their beauty and the wealth of information they can provide about how ecosystems function.

An interesting lesson demonstrated at Point Loma concerns the role of fire in chaparral and coastal sage scrub. Large, human-caused fires recur at twenty- to thirty-year intervals in southern California. We have come to believe that this fire frequency is "natural," and that the vegetation requires frequent fire for rejuvenation. In fact, recent research shows that California chaparral and coastal sage scrub most likely evolved in response to fires occurring more than 70 years apart. Furthermore, fire may be more rare in coastal areas where lightning strikes are uncommon and the relative humidity is high.

A study of burn scars shows that some shrubs in Cabrillo National Monument are at least seventy to eighty years old. The stems of one resprouting holly-leaved cherry (*Prunus ilicifolia*) are about 250 years old. Plant community studies at Point Loma show that unburned scrub can be healthy and vigorous. In addition, the unusually high density of succulents may reflect the long-term absence of fire. Most of the succulents would disappear with frequent burning, since they grow slowly and require a long time to reach maturity and produce seed. Hence, the Baja succulents occur on Point Loma because the mild climate allows their northward range extension; but they are preserved in the flora partly because of infrequent fires. Finally, some of the larger wart-stemmed ceanothus plants in the national monument develop new roots where their stems touch the ground. This growth mechanism has not been seen in younger stands, an apparent adaptation for canopy expansion in older communities when plants are crowded by their neighbors.

CONSERVATION CHALLENGES

Point Loma supports some of the best Mediterranean scrub in coastal California today. The remaining native vegetation generally is in good condition, providing excellent raw materials for continued conservation. It has been protected from grazing and frequent fire through a fortunate combination of natural geography and land management. The biggest conservation problems at the Reserve today are weed invasions, community degradation in openings and at the edges of native stands, potential loss of small and isolated populations of a few rare species, and air pollution. The responsible and ecologically sound use of fire will be an issue for management to consider. Problems inherited from the past include the reduction of the natural area to a small isolated remnant lacking any connection to other native lands; loss of habitat on the Point to development; internal fragmentation by roads, trails and facilities; the introduction of weeds through landscaping; and surface disturbance that hastened the establishment of invasive weeds. Management staff can use the science of conservation biology to help identify actions to prevent declines in at-risk plants and animals, curb weed invasions, and promote recovery of disturbed habitats.

SMALL RESERVE SIZE AND ISOLATION Worldwide, it is becoming all too familiar to see once-widespread native systems reduced to remnants. Aerial landscape views readily show the limited acreage and isolation, conditions that commonly contribute to ecological degradation in these places. The theory of island biogeography, developed in studies of oceanic islands, can help explain the effects of small size and isolation. The theory says that the smaller and farther away from the mainland that an island is, the fewer species it has. This is because many species have trouble getting to faraway places. And once they do get there, the habitats are often already occupied by ecologically similar species—a phenomenon called species saturation. Larger islands with more different kinds of habitats can support more species. Another phenomenon seen on small islands is a lack of resilience—once a species is lost, the chances of recolonization are slim, especially if that species lacks a way to travel long distances over water.

Island biogeography theory explains how islands become colonized and why they often support fewer species than similar mainland areas. Scientists are finding that the process works in reverse, too, for places like the Point Loma Ecological Reserve that have become small and isolated. These places lose species and resilience as habitat complexity and land area are reduced, distance from other natural areas is increased, and connections with nearby natural areas are lost. Clearly, much of the damage has already been done on Point Loma. Large- and medium-

LICHEN AS INDICATORS OF AIR POLLUTION

Lichen are "plants" that are really organisms made of fungi growing with cells of algae or cyanobacteria. They live together in a mutually beneficial relationship, called symbiosis, which allows them to survive in some of the harshest environments on Earth. They grow very slowly and can reach incredible ages—judging from their size and growth rates, some lichens may be thousands of years old!

Lichens absorb water and most of their mineral nutrients from the air, but they cannot excrete the elements they absorb. Some of the oxides in air pollution disrupt the metabolic pathways that make chlorophyll. Over the years these compounds accumulate in the tissues of a lichen and can weaken and kill it. Analyses of trace elements in the tissue have been used to monitor the movements of pollutants.

Evernia prunastri is a pollution-sensitive lichen no longer found in California's San Gabriel and San Bernardino mountains. It was collected at Point Loma in the early 1900s, but has not been seen since. Transplants from Santa Barbara County have not survived at Cabrillo National Monument. This is one species that apparently has succumbed to air pollution on Point Loma.

sized mammals that once roamed Point Loma and other parts of San Diego County have been gone a long time from the peninsula and surrounding area—the first animals to succumb to shrinking habitat size and connectivity in most reserves. And a small bird, the California gnatcatcher, requiring undisturbed tracts of coastal sage scrub habitat, has been seen only rarely in recent years. Several species of reptiles and amphibians also have been lost. So far, no vascular plant species that we know of have disappeared from Point Loma since botanists began recording plant survey information in the late 1800s. However, a few rare plants occur in small isolated populations that are at risk of local decline unless carefully managed. Several lichens have disappeared from the Point, probably from the combined effects of isolation, small population size, and air pollution. The challenge is to find ways to prevent further reduction in Reserve size, preserve and recover the full spectrum of natural habitat diversity possible, and assist declining species with recolonization if necessary.

HABITAT FRAGMENTATION AND EDGE EFFECTS Habitat fragmentation occurs when native areas are cut into smaller and smaller units by land development. Fragmentation can damage native habitats for plants and animals in several ways. The effects of buildings, concrete or asphalt structures are obvious: plants and animals can no longer live there. But even minor openings or disruptions in the vegetation, such as those caused by landscaping, roads, ditches, trails, or small clearings, can cause damaging changes in microhabitat conditions. Changes in environmental factors, like sun exposure, relative humidity, soil moisture, and soil structure, can make conditions bad for native seed germination and plant growth. Further, even small disturbances can isolate individuals from their neighbors, cutting off pollen flow among plants or access to mates among animals. Disturbances thus become barriers to gene flow and reproduction within populations. Finally, habitat fragmentation opens the plant community to invasion by weedy species that outcompete natives on open sites and on sites where soil disturbance is common.

A related ecological phenomenon widely studied by landscape ecologists occurs wherever native plant communities share a boundary with developed sites. There, changes in native plant species composition, plant cover, and community structure can be seen. These changes, called edge effects, extend into the community from the disturbance edge. They are common worldwide where native vegetation forms a mosaic with nonnative cover.

Disturbed sites like this World War I installation demonstrate habitat fragmentation.

The cumulative results of fragmentation and edge effects seen at Point Loma are weed invasions, soil erosion, endangerment of Orcutt's spineflower, and loss of several animal species. Luckily for the Reserve, internal habitat fragmentation has not been as bad as in many other coastal scrub natural areas, because plant cover here was preserved as camouflage for military operations through most of the twentieth century. This is the single biggest factor contributing to the overall high quality of the Point Loma scrub. Management should continue to be vigilant in preventing fragmentation and reducing edges. It would be even better to restore community integrity by removing facilities and returning open sites to native cover.

WEED INVASION The most pervasive conservation problem for the native scrub on Point Loma is invasion by nonnative plants. All the plant communities harbor weeds from other parts of the world. Nearly one quarter of the plants on the Reserve species list are foreign. The occurrence of weeds has far-reaching effects on plant and animal populations and on processes that helped shape ecological plant adaptations. The weeds were introduced either by accident—hidden on vehicles, animals, and materials brought onto the Point—or on purpose through landscape plantings. Many of them are annuals from other Mediterranean climate areas of the world, and these can quickly occupy open sites and edges in the absence of their natural predators and competitors. Some, particularly those escaped from horticulture, are perennials with mechanisms for vigorous vegetative spread or long-distance seed dispersal.

Whatever the source, these plants have insinuated themselves into the native vegetation wherever openings allowed. They often compete better for water, nutrients, and light, excluding natives from the spot. They change community structure by filling in the ground layer and closing naturally open sites, like the rock outcrops used by native cacti. Changes in community structure have cascading effects on plant and animal populations that require native microhabitats. Through their presence, nonnatives alter processes like fire, which burns hotter and more completely in vegetation with more fine fuels. Finally, they change the aesthetic experience of the Mediterranean vegetation by making it less distinctive from other weed-infested places.

For all these reasons weeds are undesirable, and a conservation goal should be to get rid of them. But, what can be done practically? It may be impossible to rid Point Loma of many weed species, but inroads can be made in several areas. First, opportunities for further introduction can be minimized. Healing disturbances and edges by restoring native plant cover will reduce the area available for weed colonization. Preventing additional disturbances will protect intact vegetation. Particular weedy disturbed areas that serve as on-site reservoirs for weed seed dispersal can be targeted for active restoration to natives. One such area, where work has already begun, is the site near the tidepools exhibit in Cabrillo National Monument that was scalped during facilities construction in the 1940s. Escaped landscape plants can be selectively attacked by cutting or treating with herbicides so they do not continue to broadcast seeds. For example, Australian eucalyptus (*Eucalyptus* spp.) and acacia (*Acacia* spp.) trees have been nearly eradicated by Cabrillo National Monument staff. Carpets of *Carpobrotus edulis* have been removed where they were planted on slopes around parking lots and other visitor facilities, and natives are being planted in these sites.

Weed reduction should be done where they are encroaching on areas of critical habitat for rare plants and animals. Finally, it will be important to monitor continually for new occurrences of aggressive weeds. This will have to be an ongoing conservation priority as long as Point Loma is open to visitors and vehicles. In the final analysis, weed control may well be one of the biggest conservation issues in the twenty-first century, as increased global exchange brings species together from all parts of the world.

The Point Loma Ecological Reserve stands out in aerial views as an isolated island of native vegetation in an urban landscape. Such views vividly illustrate the value of the Reserve for conservation and as green space for residents of San Diego. But they also remind us of habitat loss in California and other areas of the world where Mediterranean climate has influenced the development of a beautiful and rare kind of vegetation. The old-growth scrub of Point Loma really is a treasure—for the ecological lessons it teaches us, for the global connections it demonstrates, and for its beauty as it changes through the seasons.

Point Loma's diverse plant communities provide habitat for an interesting group of animals. Plants feed and shelter animals and help shape the interactions between species. Animals also respond to Point Loma as if it were an island rather than a peninsula, and that has affected their adaptations through evolutionary time.

REFERENCES/ADDITIONAL READING

Barbour, Michael, Bruce Pavlik, Susan Lindstrom and Frank Drysdale. 1993. *California's Changing Landscapes: Diversity and Conservation of California Vegetation*. California Native Plant Society Press, Sacramento. 224 pp. Beautifully written and illustrated guide to native landscapes of California.

Cuero, Delfina. 1991. *Delfina Cuero: Her Autobiography, and Account of Her Last Years, and Her Ethnobotanic Contributions*. Florence Connolly Shipek. Ballena Press, Menlo Park. 98 pp. An autobiographical account of Native American lifestyles and the landscapes of southern California and northern Baja in the early 1900s.

Dallman, Peter R. 1998. *Plant Life in the World's Mediterranean Climates*. University of California Press, Berkeley. 257 pp. A fascinating description of Mediterranean vegetation, with travel tips and beautiful illustrations. Written for lay readers.

Hickman, James C. ed. 1993. *The Jepson Manual: Higher Plants of California*. University of California Press, Berkeley. 1400 pp. The most comprehensive taxonomic guide to nearly 8,000 California plants, uses dichotomous keys to the plants using key traits, requires some botanical knowledge. Excellent illustrations of about 4,000 plants.

ORGANIZATIONS

California Native Plant Society,
1722 J St., Suite 17,
Sacramento, California 95814

A nonprofit organization dedicated to the understanding, appreciation, and preservation of California's native plants. A statewide organization with active local chapters, CNPS hosts monthly local chapter meetings, workshops, hikes, and volunteer work projects; sponsors publication of books and posters; holds an annual statewide meeting.

Excellent source of information on rare plants and habitats in California with a web site at www.cnps.org.

California Exotic Plant Pest Council,
32912 Calle del Tesoro,
San Juan Capistrano, California 92675-4427.
A nonprofit organization of professional scientists, land managers, and individuals concerned about the spread of invasive exotic vegetation in California. CalEPPC holds annual meetings, workshops and volunteer trips; publishes lists of California's worst weeds; sponsors research on control. Informative web site on weeds at www.caleppc.org

Life on the "Island": Animals

Though Point Loma is a peninsula, to land animals it is (and was) basically an island. Water surrounds it on three sides, and historically marshland likely bordered on the north where Mission Bay and San Diego Bay merged. Now the marshlands are mostly gone, the San Diego River is channelized, and the peninsula is cut off by houses on the north side.

This means isolation for animals, except for some mammals and those animals that can fly—such as birds, bats, and most butterflies. As with most islands, the peninsula has lower biological diversity when compared to the mainland hillsides. Among vertebrates, Point Loma counts 20 species of mammals, 12 species of reptiles, 1 amphibian, and more than 250 species of birds.

As a result of fragmentation and urbanization, many species have been lost from Point Loma. Nonnative species have come on the scene as well, and that has significant implications for native animals on an "island." Understanding the species that occur on Point Loma today, their interactions with each other, and the impacts of humans on the ecosystem are immediate challenges to the long-term maintenance of the peninsula's animal populations.

AUTHOR

Dr. Robert Fisher is a biologist with the U.S. Geological Survey in San Diego. He has been studying the effects of urbanization on animal communities in southern California since 1995. Much of this work has focused on reptiles and amphibians, and declines in several species have been documented as part of his work.

INTERACTIONS BETWEEN SPECIES

Most terrestrial food webs are shown as predator driven, with large carnivores and raptors at the top of the food chain, dropping down to mid-sized predators and large herbivores, then farther down still to smaller predators, and at the bottom the smallest herbivores, detritivores, and fungi. A top carnivore—the mountain lion—exists on the mainland, but Point

Loma probably never had permanent populations of mountain lions. Instead, gray foxes and bobcats historically filled that role. Coyotes returned in the mid 1990s, most likely arriving at Point Loma by way of the San Diego River. With the entry of a few coyotes, which have now become more common, the gray fox has become much less obvious on Point Loma. Research in

urban canyons around San Diego has shown that gray foxes will live pretty much anywhere, but coyotes need larger territory. And, where coyotes are present foxes are excluded. These two species have very different diets, and changes in their abundance may affect other levels of the food chain.

Along with the occasional mountain lion, archaeological data for the peninsula indicates that before European settlement pronghorn, mule deer, jackrabbit, kit fox, and badger were also present. No deer currently live on Point Loma, leaving the desert cottontail as the largest herbivore.

The gray fox may be seen along the Bayside Trail and near the tidepools.

NATIVE SPECIES

MAMMALS A tiny mammal, the desert shrew (*Notiosorex crawfordi*), is the most common shrew known from Point Loma and San Diego. While most shrews live in wet, cold environments, the desert shrew is adapted to the dry slopes and lives in a variety of different habitats. It is a voracious eater. Though rarely seen, springtime is when they are most active, probably tracking the seasonal abundance of insects, which in turn determines the peak of the shrews' abundance. Desert shrews exude a strong musky smell.

Pocket mice (*Cheatodipus fallax*), close relatives of kangaroo rats, have pockets in their cheeks where they store seeds. They also have rough spines scattered within their fur, mostly at the rump. Unlike other common rodents of Point Loma, this species is most abundant in the summer, rather than in winter or spring.

The California mouse (*Peromyscus californicus*) is the largest white-footed mouse in the country, so big it often is mistaken for a small woodrat. In fact, the California mouse is also called the parasitic mouse because it adopts nests of woodrats (*Neotoma*) as its own home. Some woodrat homes are used over many centuries.

Desert shrews are difficult to see because they are secretive. Special traps are needed to capture them.

A number of bat species were found historically around the Point Loma area. Only a few species appear to be present now. The bat species found recently around Point Loma have life history characteristics suited for life in fragmented areas of San Diego County. One species found historically around Point Loma, the Mexican long-tongued bat (*Choeronycteris mexicana*), feeds on the nectar and pollen of various plants including the Shaw's agave (*Agave shawii*). Only a few scattered Shaw's agaves remain on the Point Loma peninsula. Many types of bats typically rely on sonar to navigate and hunt for prey in the dark. It is possible signals from the Navy's research facilities at Point Loma interfere with bats' ability to use sonar in areas where signals are transmitted.

Coyotes have returned to the Point Loma in recent years, and they seem to prefer the northern portion of the peninsula.

Among larger mammals, the coyote (*Canis latrans*) seems to prefer the northern end of the peninsula, while the gray fox (*Urocyon cinereoargenteus*) is more common along the Bayside Trail and near the tidepools. The separation between the two species is consistent with research elsewhere in San Diego.

Two other mammals, raccoons (*Procyon lotor*) and striped skunks (*Mephitis mephitis*), were scattered across Point Loma. Though native, there is concern that more of them are being released by people into the Point Loma Ecological Reserve from urban areas. Efficient predators, they can prey on both terrestrial and intertidal organisms. An unnatural or higher density of these animals could create an imbalance among Point Loma's wildlife. Plus, raccoons and skunks are great vectors of parasitic worms and rabies, both of which are potentially lethal to humans.

Some birds often seen along the shore are, left to right: black oystercatcher, snowy egret, and brown pelican.

BIRDS Point Loma is touted as the best birdwatching spot in San Diego. One reason is that it serves as a "vagrant" trap for migrating species that are lost or disoriented and using the peninsula as a resting place. Often these birds are flying west instead of north to south, and many are outside their normal habitats. Some seem attracted to the ornamental vegetation on Point Loma, particularly around the cemetery. The best time to observe these unusual species, such as prothonotary warblers (*Protonotaria citrea*) and rose-breasted grosbeaks (*Pheucticus ludovicianus*), is during migrations in April and May and September and October.

Raptors use Point Loma as a migratory landmark during the peak of their migrations. Though many are common species, it is the large concentrations of them that are impressive, for example the red-tailed hawk (*Buteo jamaicensis*). Others, such as the broad-winged hawk (*Buteo platypterus*), are rare. Nearly all observations of this species in the county are from Point Loma, usually only one individual per year.

Point Loma is the only place in San Diego where black oystercatchers (*Haematopus bachmani*) are regulars. These birds prefer the undisturbed rocky shoreline on the west side of the peninsula, where they feed on mussels and limpets with their specialized bills. With black feathers and bright orange beak and eyes, these are striking birds. The American oystercatcher (*Haematopus palliatus*) is known from only one old record.

Brant's cormorant (*Phalacrocorax penicillatus*) is endemic to the California marine ecosystem. This species roosts in large numbers on the cliffs of Point Loma and La Jolla, where it finds the cliff-type vegetation it needs for cover. The males make quite a show as they try to attract mates—pointing their bills toward the sky while fluttering their wings and inflating their throat pouch. Brant's cormorant is thought to be a barometer of the abundance of the fish it feeds on. During El Niño events, reduced fish populations cause a reduction in the numbers of these birds.

A large breeding colony of black-crowned night herons exists on Point Loma.

The exotic eucalyptus woodland around the submarine base supports the most significant breeding rookery of great blue herons (*Ardea herodias*) in coastal southern California, as well as a large breeding colony of black-crowned night herons (*Nycticorax nycticorax*). These birds nest above a parking lot, leaving distinctive droppings on the vehicles. They are sensitive to disturbance, thus causing tree-trimming issues as well. One solution is to try to move these colonies to artificial nest trees, but ensuring the birds will use them is difficult. Another problem in this colony is the presence of steatites (yellow fat disease), an affliction apparently caused by nutritional deficien-

cies that kills juvenile herons.

The orange-crowned warbler (*Vermivora celata*) is common throughout San Diego, but a breeding population is rare countywide except at Point Loma. What is most interesting

THE GOOD NEWS ABOUT PEREGRINES

Historically, peregrine falcons (*Falco peregrinus*) nested successfully at Point Loma and on the nearby Los Coronados Islands in Mexico. But use of the pesticide DDT caused thinning of their eggshells, and the eggs broke during incubation. This reproductive disaster caused peregrines to become endangered across the country. Yet, extensive captive breeding and reintroductions have brought them back. For the last two decades a "hack" release site has been maintained on the tip of the peninsula. This site has been very successful and may be the sole source of peregrines now observed commonly around San Diego Bay. Peregrine falcons have been removed from the endangered species list.

about this population is that it is the Channel Island subspecies (*sordida*), which is found only there, on Point Loma, and on the Palos Verdes Peninsula. Like many other warblers, the orange-crowned gleans insects from leaves and foliage, particularly in scrub and chaparral habitats.

Song sparrows (*Zonotrichia melodia*) are common in humid habitats around the county, including along streams, marshes, and lakes. Although Point Loma lacks these habitats, this species is very common here as well. Apparently the song sparrow has adapted locally to using coastal sage scrub, as it also has done on Santa Cruz Island.

INVERTEBRATES Point Loma has a number of interesting terrestrial invertebrates, including many insects, spiders, millipedes, centipedes and a snail. Surveys in the 1990s revealed some discoveries of species new to science. One is a trap door spider in the genus *Aptostichus*, thought to be endemic to Point Loma—it lives here and nowhere else. Almost nothing is known of this relatively large spider.

Along trails in the coastal sage scrub, a black beetle scurries by with its rear in the air. These are stink beetles of the genus *Eleodes*, which spray an offensive substance if bothered. They can be watched from a distance and eventually will continue on their way. They are unique among local beetles for their daytime activity.

This large spider in the genus *Aptostichus* appears to be an undescribed species limited to Point Loma.

Two species of glowworms (*Zarhipis* spp.) have been found at Point Loma. These are beetle larvae with lateral rows of yellow or red spots that make them luminescent. Unlike other beetle larvae, they feed on large millipedes. The larva curls around the millipede like a snake and enters through the head. It then eats through the millipede, leaving only the exoskeleton behind. The other amazing thing is that the female larva never turns into a beetle like the male; instead, she matures as a giant larva sometimes more than three inches long.

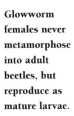

Silk-spinning crickets (*Cnemotettix miniatus*) are named for their habit of spinning silk from their mandibles to line their burrows. They build burrows in coastal sage succulent scrub and in sandy southern maritime chaparral. Before 1995, this species of cricket was known only from Catalina Island and the Tijuana Hills. Now it has been documented along the coast in small remnants of these rare habitats on Point Loma, at the Tijuana estuary, at Torrey Pines, and a few other local places. These crickets are wingless. Males

Glowworm females never metamorphose into adult beetles, but reproduce as mature larvae.

strum their back legs to call the females. The females have a very long ovipositor, almost as long as their body, with which they deposit eggs in the sand.

The Jerusalem cricket (*Stenopelmatus* spp.), sometimes called a potato bug, is another new species to science for the peninsula; previously it was known elsewhere in coastal San Diego. These large insects live under rocks and wood and are occasionally eaten by coyotes and foxes. Jerusalem crickets play an important role in the life history of the horsehair worm. This worm grows in the cricket, and when it matures it makes the cricket hydrophilic. When the cricket finds water, it will drown and the long, thin worm emerges. Large mammals such as coyotes will get the worm from drinking the water, and eventually the eggs of the worm pass out in their scat. The crickets ingest the worm while foraging in the soil, starting the cycle over again.

Shoulderband snails are most commonly seen after rains in winter.

California boasts a diversity of native terrestrial snails, with many localized species including the shoulderband snail (*Helmenthoglipta* spp.). Most of the year, they stay closed up beneath rocks and logs, but during the rainy season they come out at night. Their shells are flatter than those of garden snails, and some species have very dark or even black flesh.

REPTILES AND AMPHIBIANS No frogs are known from Point Loma, although several species would have been found along the San Diego River. They also may have inhabited vernal pools on the level parts of the peninsula along Catalina Boulevard, but the area is now totally developed. The Pacific treefrog (*Hyla regilla*), western toad (*Bufo boreas*), and western spadefoot toad (*Spea hammondii*) are among those that could have been present, but we have no known records for any of them.

The single amphibian on Point Loma today is the garden slender salamander (*Batrachoseps major*). At first glance, this species looks much like a large earthworm, until you see the tiny feet and big eyes. Garden slender salamanders are widespread across a variety of habitats and are most active on wet winter nights. They disappear during the rest of the year, probably living underground along the roots of plants. Though highly sensitive to drying, they will drown rapidly if placed in water, as they are lungless and breathe through their skin. Unlike most familiar amphibians, this species lays eggs on land that hatch into tiny salamanders; there is no free-living larval stage. This adaptation, called direct development, helps this salamander live in arid environments where ponds are absent. This species also drops its tail under duress. The tail continues to move, diverting a predator's attention, while the salamander escapes with its body. The tail will grow back over time.

Garden slender salamanders occur commonly in natural and developed areas.

Many lizards employ the tail-loss strategy too. The San Diego alligator lizard (*Elgaria multicarinata*) practices a variation on this theme. While being attacked, this lizard sometimes bites its own tail to form a loop, making it more difficult for a predator to attack and swallow it. This 7-inch-long lizard (length includes tail) is the longest on the coast; its name comes from the body shape and feisty, aggressive disposition. Alligator lizards have a long, prehensile tail used in climbing. These lizards are believed to be effective predators of black widow spiders. They seem to persist even around houses in cities, where house cats attack them. Alligator lizards often are seen on trails in early morning or late afternoon during the spring. They remain motionless until closely approached. If handled, they will attempt to bite and defecate.

The California legless lizard (*Anniella pulchra*) is the only lizard in the state that lacks legs. Though resembling a snake, its affinity with the lizards is determined by presence of eyelids and a tail that will break off. This species is rarely seen aboveground; the legless lizard spends life burrowing through sand and soil by means of a modified jaw and skull. The lower and upper jaws in most lizards end at the same point on the head. The legless lizard has a countersunk jaw—the lower jaw sits within the upper jaw, and the front of the skull usually is reinforced for pushing through sand. Also this is the only local lizard species that gives birth to two live young.

Legless lizards prefer sandy soils, where it is easy for them to burrow.

Once considered limited on the coast, the orange-throated whiptail (*Aspidoscelis hyperythrus*) has been found in other types of habitats and is more common than previously thought. This species is constantly moving and is very difficult to capture. It feeds primarily on termites dug up at the base of bushes. Males develop a striking orange throat color during the breeding season, giving the species its name. Juveniles look very different from adults—the tip of their tails is bright blue and it changes color as they grow.

The orange-throated whiptail is common in the coastal sage succulent scrub.

Two of the most commonly observed lizards on the peninsula are the western fence lizard (*Sceloporus occidentalis*) and the side-blotched lizard (*Uta stansburiana*). The western fence lizard is commonly called a "blue-belly lizard" because of the bright blue bellies found on the mature males of the species, whereas the side-blotched lizard is light colored with dark spots on the sides behind the forelimbs. The western fence lizard is the spinier and larger of the two, getting up to 3.5 inches in length. However, these closely related lizards do have similar behaviors. Both species are very active during most of the daylight hours and are often seen scurrying along trails, roadways, and buildings in and adjacent to natural lands and are commonly observed in all seasons in Point Loma.

The ring-necked snake (*Diadophis amabilis*) is small and secretive but brightly colored. While the dorsum is a light to dark green, the ventral surface is bright yellow-orange to red. Apparently ringnecks taste bad, and their vivid colors warn potential predators of this fact. The snake coils the end of its tail, exposing the brightest color, into a corkscrew and waves it overhead as part of warning behavior. When handled it may release a foul-smelling musk. This species eats salamanders, juvenile lizards, and other small snakes.

Ringneck snakes are relatively rare on Point Loma, and only a few have been seen in recent years.

The only venomous snake living on the peninsula today is the Pacific rattlesnake (*Crotalus oreganus*). The red diamond rattlesnake (*Crotalus ruber*) also occurred on Point Loma, but no confirmed observations have been recorded for decades.

Pacific rattlesnakes are seen regularly on trails and show up frequently in military buildings.

This juvenile Pacific rattlesnake shows a sharp contrast in colors, which will change as it grows.

Though these snakes serve a useful purpose by controlling rodents in buildings, people don't seem to want them around. Barrier fences can be constructed to keep rattlesnakes out of buildings, which is especially helpful where there is a lot of brush around. No roadkills of these snakes have been observed recently, although there are a few records. Compared to other local areas, where they often will rattle and strike aggressively, on Point Loma these rattlesnakes seem mild tempered. Juveniles are much more brightly colored than the adults and are often mistaken for other species of rattlesnakes.

The slender striped racer is commonly seen at Point Loma.

The striped racer (*Masticophis lateralis*) and the San Diego gopher snake (*Pituophis catenifer*) are two of the most commonly observed snakes on Point Loma. The striped racer, being active year round, can often be seen racing along the ground or through the brush in the chaparral. They are slender snakes up to 5 feet in length that are dark in coloration with lighter bellies and a white stripe on each side that runs the length of the body. The San Diego gopher snake is a stouter snake, but still reaches lengths of nearly 5 feet and has a light brown or ruddy coloration with a pattern of dark blotches on the dorsum. Both of these snakes may be commonly observed while walking along trails or driving along roads during the day.

NONNATIVE SPECIES

Because Point Loma is surrounded by urbanization, it is highly susceptible to invasion by exotic species. Birds represent the largest number of any exotic group on Point Loma, but their impacts on native species are not widely known. They range from infrequent visitors to unwanted residents, frequenting the extensive urbanized areas along the peninsula. Some of the more spectacular exotics include blue and gold macaws, which are clearly escaped pets. Other escaped pets include exotic snakes and lizards.

Studies of invertebrates in San Diego County have found that four exotic insects—Argentine ants (*Linepithema humile*), European earwigs (*Forficula auricularia*), pill bugs (*Armadillidium vulgare*), and sow bugs (*Porcellio laevis*)—may account for more than 50% of the abundance of ground-dwelling species in fragmented habitats. Argentine ants were found at almost half the

REPTILE SPECIES DIVERSITY CHANGE OVER TIME

Amphibian and Reptile species diversity changes over time. The early records are from unpublished field notes of Laurence Klauber and searches of museum records. The recent records are from our field surveys and the observation of rangers. * denotes species with XXX are known from one animal each, the Coastal Rosy Boa is discussed in the text.

COMMON NAME	Nonnative* 1920–1940s	EARLY RECORDS 1990–2000s	RECENT RECORDS
Garden Slender Salamander			
Coast Horned Lizard			
Orange-throated Whiptail			
Side-blotched Lizard			
Silvery Legless Lizard			
Southern Alligator Lizard			
Western Fence Lizard			
Spiny-tailed Iguana	XXX		
California Glossy Snake			
California King Snake			
Coastal Rosy Boa	???		
Night Snake			
Red Diamond Rattlesnake			
Red Racer			
Ring-necked Snake			
San Diego Gopher Snake			
Pacific Rattlesnake			
Striped Racer			
Western Long-nosed Snake			
Western Skink			
Western Yellow-bellied Racer			
Desert Kingsnake	XXX		

sites surveyed for ants on Point Loma. Research has shown that the diversity of native ant species greatly decreases in the presence of Argentine ants; other native invertebrates may be affected also. Impacts of the earwigs, pill bugs, and sow bugs are not known.

Two documented observations of a snake, the coastal rosy boa (*Charina trivirgata*), exist from Point Loma. Both were near the entrance to the monument, and presumably these were released pets. One of these snakes, radiotracked for more than a year, had the largest home range of a rosy boa at any natural site. The large home range has been seen in other studies of translocated snakes, as they try to learn a spatial map of a new area. This snake also inhabited bunkers on the military base, as well as exotic plants, in its daily movements.

House cats (*Felis domesticus*) have been photographed going to the tidepools, and they probably occur elsewhere in the Reserve. Feral and pet house cats have a huge impact on smaller vertebrates. They will kill many birds, lizards, and small mammals, often for sport. For cats that already have food at home, this "recreational hunting" means they could be killing many more animals than they can eat. The best management policy is to encourage homeowners to keep their cats indoors so they don't stray into natural habitat. In urban canyons around San Diego, 30% of coyote scat contained remains of house cats. Thus the presence of feral house cats in San Diego may in part be subsidizing the coyote population!

EXTINCTIONS AND TURNING BACK THE CLOCK?

Archaeological work on Point Loma has helped show which animals were here in the past. Along with information from museum collections from the beginning of the century, we now better understand the historic distributions of species and which ones are gone now. With this knowledge, we can begin to look at restoration efforts for certain species.

The coast horned lizard (*Phrynosoma coronatum*), commonly called "horny toad," once lived on the peninsula. The coast horned lizard is known from the archaeological site at Ballast Point within the last 5,000 years, which puts it near sea level, and was probably common on the top-side ridge, now almost entirely developed as roads (Catalina Boulevard and Cabrillo Memorial Drive), buildings, and the cemetery. This species has dramatically declined in recent decades throughout its range, and is apparently now extirpated on Point Loma. Horned lizards feed almost exclusively on harvester ants and live in habitats that are open at ground level for easier maneuvering. Recent ant surveys have failed to detect any harvester ant species—apparently Argentine ants have replaced them, and horned lizards will not eat Argentine ants. Argentine ants like water and tend to inhabit irrigated landscapes, often consisting of exotic plants. In southern California, *Carpobrotus edulis* is one example of an exotic, introduced for fire control and to stabilize slopes. This plant produces a high quantity of organic debris that holds moisture in the soil, and it spreads well into native habitat creating a moist environment that did not occur naturally. This moist habitat is now used by Argentine ants, and from there they expand into native scrub habitats. Removing *Carpobrotus* sp. will have direct benefits for the coast horned lizard and other native fauna. The necessary first step in recovering this species is to identify places where we should remove exotics and manage for native ants.

Horned lizards prefer chaparral and sandy habitats and have declined along the coast of southern California.

Five species of snakes are now missing from Point Loma—the glossy snake (*Arizona elegans*), red racer (*Masticophis flagellum*), western yellow-bellied racer (*Coluber constrictor*), western long-nosed snake (*Rhinocheilus lecontei*), and red diamond rattlesnake (*Crotalus ruber*). These once represented almost half the snake fauna of Point Loma, and understanding the mechanisms for their disappearance is a priority before we can restore ecosystem integrity. The two hypotheses that might explain the loss of these species are light-pollution and habitat fragmentation by roads. Because some of these species are nocturnal and apparently track the lunar cycle in their activity cycles, the urban "light bubble" around San Diego may be blotting out this nighttime celestial clue. The marine layer that often forms at night on the coast reflects light back to the ground and may be aggravating the light-pollution problem. The fragmentation caused by roads could affect movement patterns of some snakes, especially those with larger home ranges, or those that move seasonally between summer foraging areas and winter resting areas. These snakes are more likely to be killed crossing roads. Both these hypotheses need to be tested, but for now they are the best explanations we have of why snake species diversity has declined on Point Loma.

Some large mammals are also gone from Point Loma. Archaeological work shows that mule deer (*Odocoileus hemionus*) were present on the peninsula, and some naturalists remember seeing them only a few decades ago. Pronghorn (*Antilocapra americana*) were present as well and were still found on Kearny Mesa around the turn of the twentieth century. We do not know the effects of the loss of these large grazers on the peninsula's plant communities.

Mountain lions (*Puma concolor*) would have visited the peninsula on occasion, and depending on the size of the deer herd some lions could have been residents. In southern California, deer account for more than half of the lion diet, so without deer generally there are no lions. Today the amount of development around Point Loma means mountain lions could never be recovered here. Potentially deer could be brought back, and possibly bobcats could survive in limited numbers but these would be the largest mammals we could hope to recover.

A subspecies of kit fox (*Vulpes macrotis macrotis*) was endemic in coastal southern California from the Los Angeles Basin to northern Baja California, but is now extinct. There are few records for this subspecies in San Diego, the most recent being from Rancho Santa Fe early last century. The Ballast Point archaeology studies have identified this subspecies as historically inhabiting Point Loma.

The badger (*Taxidea taxus*) was also found during the archaeological work on the peninsula. This interesting species is now very rare on the coast, where it primarily occupies grasslands, meadows, and open sandy areas. It was common in the mountains and deserts of southern California, and that it used to be present on the coastline is intriguing.

The San Diego black-tailed jackrabbit (*Lepus californicus bennettii*), a giant subspecies of the widespread jackrabbit, was also detected historically on Point Loma. It is now absent along the coast except at two sites—North Island where it is abundant on the golf course and landing field, and the Tijuana estuary, where the vegetation is very short. This species, like the badger, kit fox, pronghorn, yellow-bellied racer, and red racer, would have preferred open or grassy habitat that is no longer present on the peninsula. The existing habitats are denser coastal sage scrub or chaparral. Much of the topside of the peninsula along Catalina, or the northern edges, historically may have been this type of habitat.

A bird, the greater roadrunner (*Geococcyx californianus*), apparently now is absent from Point Loma. This defining species of the West is one of the first to disappear with habitat fragmentation.

THE FUTURE

Protected areas like Point Loma face two great risks from two related forces—fragmentation and edge effects. Fragmentation divides populations of the same species within a site, putting each subpopulation—and ultimately the entire Reserve population—at a greater risk of extinction. Clearing vegetation for roads and trails, widening of trails from heavy recreational use, predation by nonnative species, and other factors lead to fragmentation and create what's called an "edge effect." Possible manifestations are erosion, reduction in available habitat for species, a change in plant communities, increased recreation, and increased fire risk.

An easy way to assess fragmentation is to measure how much edge exists around the open space of a reserve. A preliminary analysis of road edge around the open space of Point Loma showed in excess of 24 miles of pavement bordering native habitat. In contrast, the Los Coronados Islands, offshore of Tijuana and easily seen from the Point, have about the same acreage but had only a little more than 6 miles of edge, all of which is ocean. Wherever there is road, there are multiple edge effects. The most obvious is the death of animals. Reducing the road edge and fragmentation of a reserve is an important first step in increasing the chances of persistence of some species through time.

POACHING AND COLLECTION

Research on tidepools at Point Loma and elsewhere in southern California has shown that those accessible to the public are basically barren of animal life, because of people's tendency to take these animals home. On land, it is not as likely that someone will take a coyote home or put a quail in a pocket. But reptiles and amphibians are a different story. They are more vulnerable to poaching and collecting, and people need to be educated about the long-term effects of taking kingsnakes or alligator lizards from the peninsula. These species are easy to capture, and reptiles are especially popular as pets. In areas on the peninsula with high visitation, reptiles could easily be overcollected. Even a low level of removal over time may affect the viability of these species. Because of this problem, any work done to restore native snakes or horned lizards to the peninsula should take place away from main trails. Signs should be placed along trails indicating that collecting is illegal. Public education is needed on the reptiles and amphibians in general, the damage caused by removing them from their native habitat, and what has happened to the coast horned lizard specifically.

Some of Point Loma's diverse and interesting animals are gone, but some may be restorable. With active monitoring and adaptive management, the outlook for the wildlife of the peninsula is encouraging.

REFERENCES/ADDITIONAL READING

Bolger, Douglas T., Andrew V. Suarez, Kevin R. Crooks, Scott A. Morrison, Ted J. Case. 2000. Arthropods in urban habitat fragments in southern California: area, age, and edge effects. *Ecological Applications* 10:1230–1248.

Crooks, Kevin R. and Michael E. Soule. 1999. Mesopredator release and avifaunal extinctions in a fragmented system. *Nature* 400: 563–566.

Fisher, Robert, Andrew Suarez, and Ted Case. 2002. Spatial patterns in the abundance of the coastal horned lizard. *Conservation Biology* 16: 205–215.

Forman, Richard and Lauren Alexander. 1998. Roads and their major ecological effects. *Annual Review of Ecology and Systematics* 29:207–231.

Powell, Jerry and Charles Hogue. 1979. *California Insects.* University of California Press, Berkeley. 388 pp.

Stebbins, Robert C. 1985. *A Field Guide to Western Reptiles and Amphibians.* Houghton Mifflin, Boston. 336 pp.

Suarez, Andrew W., Douglas T. Bogler, and Ted J. Case. 1998. Effects of fragmentation and invasion on native ant communities on coastal southern California. *Ecology* 79: 2041–2056.

Unitt, Philip. 1984. *The Birds of San Diego County.* San Diego Society of Natural History Memoir 13. San Diego. 276 pp.

People on Point Loma: History of Human Impacts

Many people come to Point Loma to get away from it all. This remnant of San Diego coastal habitat is a peaceful place to take a hike, visit the tidepools, or just sit and stare at the ocean, yielding to the healing powers of nature. In the last 150 years the population of San Diego has exploded from 500 to around 1,500,000, a 3,000-fold increase. It is now among the ten largest cities in the country, not to mention the 35 million tourists who come each year.

What might Point Loma have been like before all the people, planes, ships, cars, and roads? What would you have seen or heard here 500, or even 5,000, years ago? And what are some of the causes and ecological consequences of all those human impacts?

PREHISTORIC POINT LOMA

AUTHOR

Samantha Weber was the first Chief of the Natural Resource Science Division at Cabrillo National Monument. She has a master's degree in conservation biology, has since worked at Yosemite National Park, and most recently is the Inventory and Monitoring Coordinator for seven parks in the Pacific Northwest.

Thousands of years ago, as humans began spreading to and through "new" continents around the planet, there was a concurrent retreat and, in many cases, extinction of very large animals such as sabertooth tigers and woolly mammoths. This disappearing act can be partially attributed to climate changes, but some theorists point a finger at a new species who came onto the scene—the smart, skinny, tool-using human. Not fast moving, but quick thinking, persistent, and armed with an opposable thumb, humans proved to be most effective manipulators of the environment, whether hunting,

gathering, or sowing seeds. And the effects of their presence on the environment continue to be felt today.

An example of historic aboriginal human impact comes from San Clemente Island, about 65 miles northwest of Point Loma.

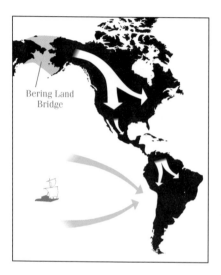

Many shell middens were left behind by aboriginal people who lived there from 300 to 2,900 years ago. The shells were from black abalone, the "single most valuable component of the shellfish economy," according to archaeologists. But this food resource was easily exhausted, and with its depletion the San Clemente islanders started eating more turban snails. What they ate was determined by what naturally grew around them and what tasted good. But they also ate what was available after their own foraging activities affected resources. The unusually large number of middens suggests that to maintain access to sufficient abalone supplies, people had to keep moving to different places on the island.

Human migration routes into the New World.

WHAT LIES BENEATH

From excavations at Ballast Point on Point Loma, we know that aboriginals lived here from about 6,600 to 1,300 years ago. The only major archaeological site investigated on Point Loma or adjacent to San Diego Bay, Ballast Point has yielded more than 5,000 years of data on climate, geology, flora, fauna, the economy, and the changes that occurred during those millennia.

Major changes swept through the intertidal zone, the shoreline between low and high tides. Initially, when sea level was much lower than it is today, a drowned stream channel flanked by mud and sand levees separated Ballast Point from North Island. North Island was the site of a freshwater spring;

the occupants of Ballast Point could fairly easily get across the channel to this spring for fresh water supplies. As sea level rose, San Diego Bay enlarged, the channel deepened and developed swift currents, and a rocky shore replaced the soft substrates near Ballast Point. Tidal flats and marshlands retreated up the embayment away from Ballast Point.

This compound fishhook was typical of that used by ancestral people of the California coast.

Prehistoric Point Lomans enjoyed much the same climate that we do today. Vegetation consisted of coastal sage scrub, coastal strand, and coastal salt marsh, and it didn't change much during the 5,000 years of site occupation. There was probably a great deal of scrub oak (*Quercus dumosa*), along with members of the mallow and evening primrose families. Pollen samples indicate that a salt marsh was probably nearby, but it continued to move farther away through time.

These ancestral people used stone-age tools. Extremely sharp hooks and spears were fashioned out of stone, animal bones, and possibly even cactus spines (if hints from more modern Kumeyaay people can be used). Cactus spines and other vegetable material do not preserve as well as stone or bone, so they are not represented in the Ballast Point record.

Fishhooks were also fashioned from shells.

Archaeologists surmised that, taking advantage of the tides, people easily could have paddled out on rafts to the kelp beds to fish, and back to Ballast Point. Indeed, accounts by early European visitors described the Native Americans as extremely skillful navigators and fishermen, rarely missing the mark with their sharp spears. Grinding tools, hearths, and bits of cooking pots were found at this site. Few bones showed burn marks (evidence of roasting), so food may have been stewed or crushed whole and then cooked, or prepared some other way. Small animals were probably crushed and eaten, bones and all, which would have increased the nutrition and flavor from added calcium and fat.

Based on bone finds (including 12,425 fish bones), we can surmise that Point Loma was used for fishing and hunting throughout the year. Early Point Lomans collected a wide variety of animal life, but in contrast to other archaeological sites in San Diego County, evidence for fish and shellfish was much more impressive in quantity and diversity than for land species. Ballast Point occupants foraged in a variety of marine habitats, including the rocky coast, kelp, soft sloughs, and sandy tidal areas. Among the thirty-six species of fish found, sheephead were the big favorite (and a major urchin predator); smoothhound sharks, shovel-nosed guitarfish, bat ray, and pile surfperch were also prevalent. The most common of the sixty-four shellfish species were clams, chitons, turban shells, and mussels. Also unearthed were olive shells that had been fashioned into beads. Shellfish collected from the nearby rocky shore and bay/estuary habitats changed through time. Over the centuries, the diversity of the shellfish collected decreased dramatically (by 50%), and the collection of rocky shore species increased. The increase in rocky shore species collected matches the geologic changes for the time period, when rising sea levels pushed back wetlands and created more rocky intertidal habitat near Ballast Point.

The most common mammal species encountered in the middens were small land mammals, especially rabbit, and marine mammals such as sea otter and sea lion. Unlike other San Diego archaeological sites, at the Ballast Point site marine mammal bones are common. Other animal remains included mountain lion, southern mule deer, kit fox, badger, southern fur seal, harbor seal, reptile (mostly rattlesnake), crab, and bird. Not all these species necessarily lived on Point Loma. Badger pelts (with bones), for example, may have been brought in by the aboriginal people to serve a particular purpose. Whole skins of badgers and raccoons have been used by contemporary Native Americans for arrow quivers and other special containers. Yet what we see is that human experience on Point Loma long ago involved a rich array of native wildlife: from shellfish to seals in the sea to quail and mountain lions on land.

EUROPEAN CONTACT

Accounts by the first European explorers who came to San Diego invariably included a description of the Native Americans they encountered on or around Point Loma, whether the year was 1542, 1602, or 1769. Usually, the native people were described as peaceful and eager to trade, after some initial and understandable apprehension was overcome. Thus began the early and long history of trade in the port of San Diego. The native Kumeyaay people traded sea-otter pelts and other highly prized skins to the Spaniards in exchange for beads and other goods they desired.

The Kumeyaay Indians, who lived in southern California, were skilled manipulators of their environment. They developed water control systems and practiced burning and agriculture to increase the availability of desirable resources. According to translator Florence Shipek, "In the upper portions of some mountain valleys, the Spanish saw 'acequias' and noted that the 'pasture' was 'irrigado' . . . . In Southern California, the Spanish saw—but failed to recognize—a system of planting, harvesting, and managing the environment that was very different from that practiced in Europe; they therefore claimed that the native peoples only gathered what 'nature' produced."

A Kumeyaay family near Warner Springs illustrated by Arthur Aschott in the 1857 Emory Report.

Point Loma had special importance in Kumeyaay life because of its physical shape and its rich resources, both on land and in the sea. They could hunt on land, fish in the sea, and harvest plants. Consistent with the archaeological records is the account in the 1769 narrative of Spanish explorer Miguel Costansó: "Fish constitutes the principle [*sic*] food of the Indians who inhabit the shore of this port, and they consume much shellfish because of the greater ease they have in procuring them. They use rafts made of reeds, which they manage dexterously by means of a paddle or double-bladed oar. Their harpoons are several yards long, and the point is a very sharp bone inserted in the wood; they are so adroit in throwing this weapon that they very seldom miss their mark."

AUGUST DUHAUT-CILLY AT POINT LOMA

Duhaut-Cilly, the Frenchman who visited in 1827, remarked on the extensive giant kelp beds just off Point Loma. Although the kelp forest (Macrocystis) is still one of the largest in the world, at that time the kelp beds reached even farther south, stretching beyond the mouth of San Diego Bay. The physical extent of these kelp beds is surprisingly well documented due to early maps, which were a priority because the beds could be a navigational hazard. An 1857 chart shows a huge kelp bed, about one quarter of which extended beyond the southern tip of Point Loma, and the northern edge reaching just beyond the historic entrance to Mission Bay (then False Bay).

August Duhaut-Cilly, a Frenchman who sailed into San Diego Bay in 1827, watched Native Americans in organized hunts on Point Loma. Two-to-three hundred Kumeyaay would form a human line from the steep bluffs to the shore and, advancing together with curved throwing sticks, drive rabbits and hares ahead of them into gullies or up against walls. As Duhaut-Cilly described, "Some seek vainly to climb the wall on the right; others hurl themselves into the bay; there are some [hares and rabbits], and these are the only ones, to have any chance of safety, which attempt to run through the adverse front; it is a general massacre. . . in which many always perish before the remainder can pierce through the line of the Indians."

Duhaut-Cilly himself did some hunting on the Point, describing abundant game of all sorts. "Hardly had we put foot on shore when on all sides, to the right and to the left, we stirred up great bevies of quail. . . .Hares and rabbits moved in bands across the fragrant and flowering fields that carpeted the slope of the hill. In the midst of such great numbers there was no need for a hunting dog. . . .In respect to this game Point Loma is a more favored spot than the surrounding country, which is much less populated." Rabbits still abound on Point Loma, though no "hares" (black-tailed jackrabbits) remain. Duhaut-Cilly also described roadrunners living "in the vicinity of the anchorage" at the time, saying they ran as fast as a horse. Unfortunately, the roadrunners are gone now too.

Ancient Indian trails crisscrossed Point Loma, greeting Juan Rodríguez Cabrillo and his successors. They ran from the La Playa shore on the east side, to the top of the ridge, and down to the western tidepools. Some modern roads follow the path of some of these old trails, like Cañon and Rosecrans streets (the latter covers part of the historic La Playa trail). San Diego historian Winifred Davidson noted that when a road swings left or right for no apparent reason, it may be following the same route as an ancient trail that was turning to avoid a barrier such as a rock outcrop or stream. The existence of these historic trails attests to the long-standing importance of Point Loma to Native Americans.

CAN'T SEE THE FOREST FOR THE TREES

The existence of an oak forest on Point Loma at the time of European contact is a matter of some dispute. Cabrillo, ever mysterious, does not contribute to the fray. Sebastían Vizcaíno, commanding the second European voyage to San Diego in 1602, mentioned good wood but was not specific. In 1769, Father

Junípero Serra said that wood was scarce in the immediate area, although arroyos were overgrown with trees. Serra and his companions were the first Europeans to take up residence, so any large-scale European-induced changes to an existing Point Loma "forest" probably occurred after their arrival. That same year Gaspar de Portolá, a Spanish soldier and first governor of California, and Miguel Costansó, an engineer and cartographer, agreed that cottonwoods were growing near the river, but they were leagues away (a league back then was usually about 4.5 miles). In 1776, missionary and cartographer Pedro Font said the area was very short of firewood. Archibald Menzies, a Scottish

Artist Richard Schlecht's conception of the landing of Juan Rodriguez Cabrillo in 1542.

botanist with the George Vancouver expedition that visited San Diego in 1792, stated that there were no trees anywhere around, and described Point Loma as mostly covered by shrubbery and brushwood.

Sixty-six years after the Serra settlement, Richard Henry Dana in *Two Years Before the Mast* described Point Loma as well wooded, although that first assessment was made from a ship approaching the Point at sunset. Later, when Dana actually lived on La Playa in Point Loma—up to his eyeballs in the hide trade—he said there were no trees of any size for miles. This had become an issue for him because he had to collect wood for the camp cook. Dana did not enjoy hiking farther and farther from camp, into Point Loma as time went on, to find and chop suitable brush and small trees and haul them on his back. He complained that the task was all the more vexing because the wood available was mostly twigs and branches.

In 1850, a surveyor said that wood came from 8 to 10 miles away, and historian Winifred Davidson described Point Loma

in 1880 as covered with coarse grass, cacti, wild sage, and low bushes. Contrary to most of the eighteenth- and nineteenth-century reports, a couple of old-timers in the twentieth century told of a forest. But even they said that any stumps left after the trees were cut or burned were dug up and burned for firewood by Kumeyaay. Thus, little evidence was left to prove or disprove their assertions.

A forest, though, may be in the eye of the beholder. The oaks here today are scrub oaks, closer to the shrubs and small trees Dana later described than to any towering, shade-bearing trees. Today the north-facing slopes of Point Loma support lemon-adeberry bushes (*Rhus integrifolia*) and toyon trees (*Heteromoles arbutifolia*) which, in gullies on the east side, can tower over a six-foot-tall person. The unique form of Point Loma shelters the eastern (lee) side from ocean breezes so shrubs can grow tall and thick; on the western slopes, shrubs are low and more widely spaced. And who knows what that dense growth on the eastern slopes looked like to someone on a ship passing into the harbor, under various lighting conditions, gazing through fatigued eyes while missing the forests of home?

THE BEGINNING OF SPANISH RULE

When Cabrillo landed in "San Miguel" in 1542, claiming the land for Spain, he launched the beginning of Spanish influence on the west coast of what is now the United States. When Sebastián Vizcaíno sailed into the bay in 1602, he renamed the place "San Diego" and, like Cabrillo, left to continue exploring. Vizcaíno did stay long enough to dub Ballast Point "La Punta de los Guijarros" (Cobblestone Point). The cobblestones on La Punta de los Guijarros were used for ballast in ships leaving the harbor, so the newer name matches the old.

More than 150 years later, in 1769, the first European settlers came to San Diego. Captain Gaspar de Portolá and

The early Spanish settlement of Santa Ysabel.

Franciscan Father Junípero Serra established the presidio (fort) and mission, several miles from San Diego Bay. This marked the start of the mission era, which stressed the Kumeyaay people and their culture by introducing a new religion, slavery, disease, and death. It also stressed native ecosystems.

The ruins of Mission San Diego de Alcalá, around 1887.

THE CATTLE ARE MOWING

Almost as soon as the Spaniards occupied San Diego, they altered hydrologic regimes by installing a dam at the second mission location, and introduced nonnative species of plants and animals, including cattle and exotic grasses. For a century after the founding of San Diego, cattle raising was the most economically important industry in the state. Winifred Davidson described what the scene must have been like in 1782: "Point Loma lay at the door of the Presidio dwellers. Upon it grazed their young herds of long-horned cattle and thoroughbred horses. Its trails were their bridle paths; its beaches their pleasure grounds." By 1830, some 15,000 head of cattle, 20,000 sheep, and many thousands of hogs grazed in and around San Diego. The detrimental effects of these animals on the land were soon apparent. It was reported that the immense bands of sheep trampling the wet ground had packed it to the hardness of adobe brick. Plants such as filaree and burr clover were nearly destroyed by being grazed off while growing, replaced by various grasses and weeds. However, an observer remarked in 1888 that the desolate appearance given the land by the bands of sheep could scarcely be imagined by those who looked only on the cultivated vineyards of El Cajon or the alfalfa fields of San Jacinto.

Though this description suggests drastic change, exactly how heavily herds grazed Point Loma itself is unclear. But the nonnative plants that came into San Diego are clearly now on Point Loma. A more obvious consequence of the cattle trade was development of the hide and tallow industries, which worked busily on Point Loma beaches in the mid to late 1800s.

THE HIDE AND TALLOW INDUSTRY

Hide houses stood on Ballast Point in the 1840s and figured in the whaling industry from the 1850s through the 1870s. Tallow, the fat in cows, sheep, and whales, was melted and made into candles, soap, and other goods. Although Richard Henry Dana described gathering wood for cooking in the hide houses, tallow work also demands a great deal of fuel because tallow must be melted. By contrast, hides are dried in the sun. Presumably, tallow workers were obliged to forage for wood even more than Dana and his hard-working cronies did.

Where did all the wood come from to sustain this industry? Presumably from as close as possible. Wood may have been brought in, but one can readily imagine tallow workers scouring the nearby hills of Point Loma for fuel. The amount of wood collected by tallow, hide, abalone, and whale industry workers through the decades—coupled with the impacts of cattle, mule deer, and people traveling through the same hills—could easily account for the much thinner state of Point Loma vegetation in the nineteenth and early twentieth centuries. The keepers of both lighthouses, who also had horses and cows, may also have played a role. The change to dense vegetation over the last century or so has probably been greatly influenced by the closure of Point Loma to the public at large.

When not collecting scrubby wood or scraping and curing cattle hides, Dana and presumably many other hide workers and tallowers enjoyed hunting on Point Loma and watching dogs chase after coyotes on the beach, sometimes killing them.

Occasionally Dana and friends spent their free time finding and killing rattlesnakes, which were apparently quite abundant in the area and which heightened the excitement of firewood forays. Dana also mentioned that the large population of dogs living freely on the beach at the hide-house camps kept the Indians away at night. Thus, the Kumeyaay were denied access to important resources, like marine food. The Ballast Point squatters, a culturally diverse crowd, were themselves finally evicted from Point Loma, by the American military in 1870.

OTTERS AND ABALONE AND WHALES, OH MY!

The Spanish Fort Guijarros, built in 1795.

The Spaniards began work on a fort at the base of Point Guijarros in 1795. This new fort, commonly referred to as Guijarros, was built to protect San Diego Bay from unwelcome visitors—at least those unwelcome by the Spaniards. Three years later, Fort Guijarros had eight to ten cannons and six men ready to repel British, French, or Russian ships wanting to enter the channel, not then allowed by Spanish law. This marked the beginning of a long, complicated his-tory of building and installing guns, and abandoning or dis-mantling them, on Point Loma. Much of the initial concern over control of the land was for access to important trade

The first drawing of the Point Loma Lighthouse shortly after it was constructed.

A market for whalebone used in women's fashions gave the whaling industry a boost in the late 1800s.

centers and resources, like sea otter pelts.

In 1828, the American merchant ship *Franklin* came into San Diego Bay in pursuit of a cache of sea otter skins. The ship fled after Fort Guijarros guns "inflicted considerable damage to her hull and rigging," writes Barry Joyce in *A Harbor Worth Defending*. This event marked not only the effectiveness of Mexican harbor defense (Mexico had won independence from Spain in 1821), but also the importance of the sea otter trade. Sea otters were once plentiful along the California coast, including San Diego, but they were extirpated from Point Loma. They were hunted for their soft, dense pelts, which were highly valued in China and elsewhere. So, although the human population of this coast was not great, the perceived "need" for this resource was greatly exaggerated by heavy exporting. Though a highly profitable business, it was unsustainable. Sea otters reproduce slowly, and overhunting drove them to the brink of extinction. A few otters survived the onslaught elsewhere, and populations are slowly recovering.

The ecological consequences of reduced sea otter populations, important predators in the marine food chain, are seen in middens on islands off California. Sea otters prey on sea urchins, and when Native Americans heavily hunted sea otters (and sheephead), sea urchin populations would boom. This left urchin barrens—areas with lots of urchins and little else. Evidence of historic urchin booms appears as occasional, thin layers of solid urchin shells in the middens. A similar dearth of sea otters and sheephead at the Channel Islands, and subsequent boom in urchins, may account for the smaller size of those islands' kelp beds today. The superabundant urchins would eat through vast numbers of giant kelp holdfasts, setting great quantities of kelp adrift. Kelp beds are an extremely important and relatively uncommon habitat that supports rich communities of fish and other life forms. Reducing or eliminating kelp beds can cause serious declines in the many species that depend on them.

The presence of whales and the impact of the whaling industry is nicely summarized by the San Diego Federal Writers Project:

Harvesting blubber for rendering into whale oil

Whales were a common sight in and around San Diego harbor in the early days, and by 1853 whaling began to assume economic importance. Two companies were operating from Ballast Point on Point Loma by 1863, and it was a favorite sport for the townspeople to watch from the lighthouse grounds. There were times when it was unsafe to cross the bay in a rowboat because of the number of whales, 40 having been reported as visible at

one time. Because of the increase in shipping and the ruthless hunting, whales deserted this area, and the whale-oil industry died.

Visitors still enjoy watching Pacific gray whales migrate past

Point Loma in the winter, on their journey hundreds of miles south to the warm waters of Mexico where they give birth. If a whale is discovered in San Diego Bay today it is an exciting event; many view it as a "mistake" on the part of the whale.

Much like whales and sea otters, abalone stocks have suffered from overharvest. Kumeyaay Indians ate abalone throughout the centuries, but the animals were still abundant when the Spaniards, Mexicans, and Americans arrived. During the late 1700s and early 1800s, Spanish and Mexican settlers harvested limited numbers of abalone for their shells for ornamentation, but they did not eat the meat. A great favorite of the Chinese, abalone was overfished in China by the 1850s. Demand grew for another source, and by 1856 abalone harvesting by San Diego's Chinese fishermen was documented. In about forty years, millions of abalone were harvested, dried, and shipped to China. In the 1880s, 35% of all abalone meat and 41% of all abalone shells exported from the United States were shipped from San Diego. By the end of the nineteenth century, legislation pushed the Chinese out of the abalone business. Again, an inflated and unsustainable demand for a slow-growing organism had predictable results. Today, abalones in California have declined so precipitously that no harvesting is allowed south of San Francisco, and the white abalone is now on the federal endangered species list.

ON THE POLITICAL FRONT

In 1847, while the United States and Mexico were at war, the first official census of San Diego County residents was taken. Results of this sparsely populated but diverse county showed that "the white population numbered 248; and there were 483 converted Indians, 1,550 'wild' Indians, 3 Negroes and 3 Sandwich Islanders [Hawaiians]." In that year, the average "San Diegan" was a Kumeyaay Indian. The next year, 1848, when the treaty of Guadalupe Hidalgo ended the war, Ballast

Point and all of Point Loma passed into the hands of the United States. Two years later California was admitted as a state into the Union, and in 1852 President Millard Fillmore set aside the Point Loma reservation for military use. Ballast Point, however, remained a squatter haven and a steadfast whaling community for another eighteen years.

The La Playa harbor in 1898.

Within a few years of American occupation of San Diego, large-scale, lasting changes occurred in and around Point Loma. Much of the area between today's Old Town and San Diego and Mission bays was once mudflats. In 1853, to keep San Diego Bay channel from silting in, the federal government channeled the San Diego River to run exclusively into Mission Bay. This allowed larger ships to enter San Diego Bay but choked off the centuries-old wetlands that stood between the river and the bay, irrevocably changing this once-rich estuary.

The Old Point Loma Lighthouse.

A year later construction began on the old Point Loma lighthouse. This landmark, an icon of Point Loma and San Diego, was built atop the southern end of the Point, about 400 feet above sea level. The lighthouse precipitated another ecologically significant event—construction of the first road along the ridge of Point Loma. Until then, much of the development activity had occurred on the east side, on and around Ballast Point and La Playa. Habitat fragmentation and impacts of traffic, even if it was only mule teams, was beginning to be felt in this area. The road also meant that more people could easily visit Point Loma and engage in activities like watching the whaling industry. In 1891, the "New" Point Loma lighthouse, located on the southwestern side of Point Loma, much closer to sea level was called into service.

Point Loma Lighthouse on Ballast Point, built in 1891.

THE MILITARY TAKES OVER

In 1898, during the Spanish-American War, all civilians, including Native Americans, were excluded from Point Loma. Military personnel—196 men of Battery D—lived in tents on the Point. The next year, the military reservation was named Fort Rosecrans, for Civil War general and California politician William Starke Rosecrans. In 1901, the U.S. Navy started building a coaling station to the north of Fort Rosecrans. By 1903, development at the fort got the Army men out of tents and into new barracks just north of Ballast Point. In 1905, the Army Corps of Engineers built the Zúñiga jetty to prevent resilting of the channel, to ensure it remained consistent and deep. To this day, the jetty probably affects and limits the southern extent of the Point Loma kelp beds.

By the early 1900s, most of today's Point Loma players were in place. The military, the U.S. Coast Guard, and the cemetery were all here in 1900. The National Park Service joined the scene when Cabrillo National Monument was created in 1913, although the military was in charge of the monument until 1933.

Forty-six structures were built from 1905 to 1945, and each one involved many men, horses, mule teams, and heavy machinery, clearing and excavating land, pouring concrete and asphalt, laying down sandbags, and bringing in metal, wood, and stone. Historic photographs show areas of white—bare earth surrounding new installations where all the vegetation was removed.

NATIVE PEOPLE: THE END OF AN ERA

The turn of the twentieth century marked the end of Native American use of Point Loma's natural resources. The people were steadily being pushed farther east, and during the Spanish-American War civilians were not allowed on Point Loma. Delfina Cuero, a Kumeyaay Indian who lived in San Diego at the turn of the century, recalled distant memories:

I can remember when I was pretty young, we used to go and look for xalyak (abalone). . . .We used to hunt for fish, shellfish, and other stuff in the ocean and along the edge of the ocean around Ocean Beach. There are so many houses here now I can't find my way anymore. [The shoreline at Ocean Beach has been filled in part.] Everything looks so bad now; the hills are cut up even. I can remember coming to mat kunyily (Point Loma). There were not many houses then.

I was little and don't remember all, but there was a lot of food here then. We had to hunt for plant food all day to find enough to eat. We ate a lot of cactus plants [and Opuntia and Dudleya]. We ate a lot of shellfish. There were lots of rabbits there too. My grandfather used to tell the boys to eat rabbit eyes especially, because it would make them good hunters. We hunted those things until we couldn't hunt on Point Loma any more.

The men working to build and man Fort Rosecrans needed to eat and often needed wood for cooking. Hunting was not only a source of food, but also of recreation. All these actions affected Point Loma plants and wildlife. Some impacts were probably immeasurably small, others may have contributed to species extirpation; for example, the last mule deer on Point Loma is rumored to have been shot by a member of the armed forces. Like the Native Americans, military men and women and other residents took advantage of the great wealth of seafood (lobster and abalone) as well. Point Loma was suddenly a backyard for many more people than it had been thousands of years before. Change was inevitable on this small parcel of land.

THERE GOES THE NEIGHBORHOOD

Wildlife was not only losing numbers and habitat on Point Loma, development also cut off their traditional movements between the Point and other undeveloped areas. Animals were running out of escape routes, and Point Loma was becoming more of an island for them. From 1900 to 1960, the population of San Diego doubled every decade. A 1928 aerial photograph shows that Point Loma was already physically isolated from other natural open space. Many sidewalks in Point Loma neighborhoods dated to this time, and the family car was just coming into vogue. Wildlife might still have been able to move to and from the Point, but exposure and risk were greater all the time.

Before the San Diego River was diverted, the river route to San Diego Bay created a watery break, called the Spanish Bight, between North Island and the rest of Coronado Island. In 1919, this break was filled with dredging deposits to increase the island by 620 acres. A naturalist of the time reported "50,000 to 100,000" brant (a type of goose) in Spanish Bight in the 1880s, and contrasted this to the species' rarity in the 1920s, attributing the difference to the fill operation. Brant can still be seen in San Diego Bay and the river, but not in such large numbers.

THE WAR YEARS

Cabrillo National Monument was established in 1913 by President Woodrow Wilson to commemorate the achievements of Juan Rodríguez Cabrillo. World War I started the next year, so Fort Rosecrans was closed to the public from 1914 through 1918. The Park Service assumed jurisdiction in 1933, with a break again during World War II, when the military closed the entire peninsula.

Beginning in the mid 1930s, the National Park Service, a land conservation agency, also planted nonnative, invasive landscaping at Cabrillo National Monument. Some of this vegetation escaped intended boundaries, displacing the native habitat.

World War II gun emplacement.

The aggressive nature of the nonnatives was undoubtedly unknown at the time, and the rarity of Point Loma habitat either was not yet an issue, or was not fully understood. In one instance, use of native plants was considered, but getting enough plants at a reasonable price proved difficult, so nonnatives were used.

During World War II, all along the West Coast, including Point Loma, gun emplacements, bunkers, and other military structures were built to protect the United States from Japanese attack. Exotic species such as *Carpobrotus* sp. and acacia were planted because they grew quickly (important for camouflaging new military installations), had a predictable physical shape, and thrived in the coastal environment.

THE CEMETERY THROUGH THE CENTURIES

In 1879, the soldiers of Company E, Ninth U.S. Infantry were sent to break a trail to the top of Point Loma for a cemetery. The first documented burial there was that same year, although there are several undocumented stories of previous burials scattered throughout Point Loma.

The new Fort Rosecrans reservation included the cemetery, which in 1883 was officially named the "Post Cemetery, San Diego Barracks (Point Loma)." The cemetery was small at first, and infrequently used. As a result, by 1887 men from Company E had to cut through brush to rebuild the road to it.

Today the cemetery has grown to sixty-five acres. This beautiful place is rich in exotic trees and shrubs, and a popular spot for sighting rare birds. Water is added to this naturally dry system, which favors nonnative plants and animals, including *Carpobrotus* sp. and Argentine ants.

So, the cemetery is an ecological mixed bag—habitat for some but no longer for others. And it may pose a movement barrier insurmountable for some. Regardless, the national cemetery is beloved for what it represents and the people and the sacrifices it honors.

After World War II, San Diego was one of the most over-crowded cities in the nation. By the 1950s and 1960s, the city was facing a sewage crisis as thousands of gallons of untreated sewage and industrial waste flowed directly into San Diego Bay. The sewage was washed out of the bay on the tides and settled right on top of the kelp forest canopy. That, combined with sea urchins mowing down the forests from the bottom up, caused a huge dieback and near disappearance of the kelp beds.

The Point Loma Wastewater Treatment Plant was built in

1963. It diverted this sewage before it entered the bay, treated it, and then released it out at sea beyond the western edge of the kelp beds. Sea urchin control efforts began (poisoning), and the results of that along with the new sewage plant can be tracked on historic maps, revealing the rebirth of the kelp forest.

The Point Loma Wastewater Treatment Plant.

As the urchin fishery developed in the 1970s, the poisoning stopped and the kelp forest was stabilized. Still, the continued dredging of San Diego and Mission bays and the influence of the Zúñiga jetty probably constrain the northern and southern extent of the beds, making it unlikely that the Point Loma kelp beds will return to their historic expanse. However, scientists say that harvesting of kelp in the Point Loma kelp forest is well managed, so is likely to remain a part of Point Loma for a very long time. Management of the animals that inhabit the kelp forest—the sea otters, abalone and sheephead—is another issue altogether.

In the 1960s, Cabrillo National Monument expanded its developed area, constructing an administration building, an auditorium, a visitor center, and a large parking lot. The parking lot and other structures were made possible by filling in canyon edges to increase available land area. Visitation soon shot up to more than one million people each year. By the 1970s, the National Park Service began to see signs that the natural resources of Cabrillo were suffering from heavy visitation and unregulated use. The park's 1976 master plan cited the heavy visitation to the tidepools as a threat for which little research had been done. Further, the plan stated that commercial fishing for spiny lobster and abalones in and around the kelp beds had reached practical limits, and raised the possibility of more stringent controls. These management issues are not settled to this day, but progress is being made.

POINT LOMA TODAY

Despite all the development in San Diego and on Point Loma over the years, Point Loma still has an impressive 900 acres of rare habitat remaining out of a total 1,500 acres. Today Point Loma is home to a large military installation, including research and support facilities, as well as historic military structures, some still in use and others abandoned. Point Loma is also home to Cabrillo National Monument, 20 acres of which are developed, and all of which are viewed by more than a million visitors a year. Also included on the Point are the Fort Rosecrans National Cemetery, the U.S. Coast Guard, and Point Loma Wastewater Treatment Plant.

Of the 900 acres of native scrub habitat, some are less than pristine. There are tracts of nonnative vegetation, old roads buried beneath fields of nonnative grasses, and even "trash" from previous military projects or exercises. Yet overall, swaths of high-quality, interesting, and biologically rich habitat remain —the natural heritage of Point Loma. This habitat is considered under the California National Diversity Database to be globally endangered, while the U.S. Fish and Wildlife Service considers all the habitat on Point Loma to be sensitive. One of the plant community types on Point Loma is represented by a worldwide expanse of fewer than 2,500 acres!

What remains here owes its existence to some of the same agencies that were responsible for significant impacts—particularly the military and the National Park Service. These agencies now own and are trying to preserve much of the natural habitat. Had the land fallen into private hands and been sold long ago, it very likely would have become the site of exclusive homes; this would have dramatically impaired its natural beauty, and would have been off limits to the public. In the end, the most significant impact humans may have on Point Loma is our ability to preserve this beautiful, rich, unique place for all to enjoy.

REFERENCES/ADDITIONAL READING

Berryman, Judy. 1999. Chinese abalone fishermen on San Clemente Island: An archaeologist's perspective. *Mains'l Haul*, Vol. 35, No. 243.

Blackburn, Thomas C. and Kat Anderson. 1993. Introduction: Managing the domesticated environment. In *Before the Wilderness: Environmental Management by Native Californians*. Ballena Press, Menlo Park.

Cuero, Delfina. 1991. *Delfina Cuero: Her Autobiography, and Account of Her Last Years, and Her Ethnobotanic Contributions*, Florence Connolly Shipek, translator. Ballena Press, Menlo Park.

Gallegos, Dennis and Carolyn Kyle. 1988. *Five Thousand Years of Maritime Subsistence at CA-SDI-48, on Ballast Point, San Diego County, California*. Coyote Press, Salinas, CA.

Joyce, Barry. 1995. *A Harbor Worth Defending*. Cabrillo National Monument Foundation, San Diego.

Leberthon and Taylor. 1888. *The City and County of San Diego*. Illustrated and containing biographical sketches of prominent men and pioneers. San Diego.

Pourade, Richard F. 1961. *The Explorers*. Union-Tribune Publishing Company, San Diego.

San Diego Federal Writers' Project. 1937. *San Diego: A California City*. Works Progress Administration, State of California, San Diego Historical Society.

Shipek, Florence. 1993. Kumeyaay plant husbandry: Fire, water, and erosion control systems. In *Before the Wilderness: Environmental Management by Native Californians*. Ballena Press, Menlo Park.

Tegner, Mia. Personal interview by author, December 2000.

Tegner et al. 1996. Is there evidence for long-term climatic change in southern California kelp forests? *California Cooperative Oceanic Fisheries Investigation Report*, Vol. 27.

Taking the Vital Signs: Monitoring and Management

The mission of the National Park Service is to "promote and regulate the use of the Federal areas known as national parks, monuments, and reservations. . .to conserve the scenery and the natural and historic objects and the wild life therein and to provide for the enjoyment of the same in such manner and by such means as will leave them unimpaired for the enjoyment of future generations."

This mission, which dates to the Park Service's creation in 1916, guides Cabrillo National Monument as well, although it was established three years earlier. The park was set aside to commemorate Juan Rodríguez Cabrillo's discovery of what is now the west coast of the United States. Thus it was founded for cultural significance—its place in the history of people—rather than for natural resources. But the park does possess natural values, some remarkable ones in fact, and those values are still here, thanks in part to the presence throughout the years of the military on Point Loma.

Priorities change, and Cabrillo represents a microcosm of changes within the National Park Service. The Park Service has both the benefit of an improved understanding of the natural environment, and the challenge of managing impacts to park resources from visitation levels unimagined in 1916.

The original half acre of Cabrillo National Monument was filled by the old Point Loma lighthouse, and cultural issues filled up the "to do" lists of the first

AUTHOR

Samantha Weber was the first Chief of the Natural Resource Science Division at Cabrillo National Monument. She has a master's degree in conservation biology, has since worked at Yosemite National Park, and most recently is the Inventory and Monitoring Coordinator for seven parks in the Pacific Northwest.

After World War II, San Diego was one of the most overcrowded cities in the United States. Rapid post World War II development isolated Point Loma natural resources from other nearby natural areas.

park managers. And why not? The lighthouse and the story of Spanish discovery were what the park was all about. Accordingly, older park planning documents seldom mentioned any efforts to preserve what are now very rare habitats. Managers in this and many other parks had to use intuition and experience to make decisions, not knowing what the impacts might be upon natural resources. The information they needed to make informed, science-based decisions seldom existed, and even if it did, park managers rarely had the resources to find, interpret, and apply that information. Park staffs were small, time was short, and thousands of visitors kept arriving day after day.

Environmental awareness blossomed in the 1960s and 1970s across the United States. A number of landmark pieces of environmental legislation were passed during this period, including the Endangered Species Act, clean air and water legislation, and the National Environmental Policy Act. These laws necessitated that the National Park Service and other federal agencies change the way they managed resources.

Evaluating the impacts of human action upon resources begins with one question: what resources? Awareness of the importance of resource preservation often preceded knowledge of what those resources were and how they should be preserved. In 1973, Cabrillo National Monument's draft master plan contained a single paragraph about the "chaparral communities" of Point Loma and one about wildlife: "Rabbits, squirrels, reptiles, rodents, stray cats and shore and land birds are the relatively few forms of wildlife on Point Loma. ...Except possibly for the shore birds, occasional sea lions, harbor seals and tidepool life, *the wildlife of the area cannot be considered as a major resource of the monument.*" [emphasis added]. In this same document, the crux of the problem was noted: "Adequate information on many aspects of the Point Loma resources is lacking. ...Basic research on the tidepools and the hillside plant and wildlife communities will be a continuing requirement." The information simply was not available. Yet that same document also observed that "continuing research is an essential element in the management concept. Sporadic research efforts would not provide adequate information for management to act in time to prevent permanent resource damage due to excessive or inappropriate visitor use."

The tide was beginning to turn. Only a year later, an entire document was dedicated to the management of the natural resources of Cabrillo National Monument. It still offered the view that the natural resources of Point Loma, save the intertidal zone, were somewhat meager: "Within the limits of the park's boundary, only a few forms of mammals can be found," and "The one reptile of note is the southern Pacific rattlesnake (*Crotalus viridis helleri*)." But planners did recognize the rich bird life, pointing out that in 1972 more than sixty-five species were observed in the park. Today, we know the number to be nearly four times that.

DATA, DATA, WHO HAS THE DATA?

Without research, how can we know if resources are "unimpaired?" The first step involves taking an inventory of what is in the park. Inventories help describe the condition of the resources in relation to a standard condition, preferably the natural or unimpaired state. A plant species inventory may note which species are nonnative (introduced) or which native species were once present but have disappeared. When those prophetic words were written in 1973 about the need for basic research, Cabrillo National Monument had no intertidal species inventory; the plant species list peaked at about thirty species, and it would be seventeen years before the first monitoring program would begin.

Dr. Joy Zedler.

In 1976, the park hired Dr. Joy Zedler of San Diego State University to conduct an inventory of the rocky intertidal area. This study provided the first scientific list of the plants and animals of Cabrillo's rocky intertidal area, a part of the park recognized for years as environmentally sensitive and important. Dr. Zedler recommended that the park begin a long-term monitoring study of the rocky intertidal area. The results of her work are still in use as very important baseline inventory data. Baseline data, in this case, is basic information on which plants and animals live in the park and how they are doing. This information is fundamental to management. It can be compared to later inventories to see if any changes have occurred—have some species disappeared, have new ones arrived?

As important as inventories are, they are not enough. Park managers need monitoring programs to detect changes in resources and the causes. Monitoring is an ongoing process designed to measure changes by sampling the resource again and again, over time. This allows trends to be detected, giving a sense of whether populations are increasing, decreasing, or holding steady. Monitoring is more powerful than some inventories because it can tell managers about a drop in abundance of a species, for example, before the species is gone. Some repeated inventories can only document species loss, as opposed to unusual decreases which can lead to intervention to prevent that loss. Well-designed monitoring programs also

allow predictions, a powerful tool for managers if the observed changes are unnatural and threaten ecosystem health.

To detect trends in population increases or declines, the resource must be sampled again and again.

WHAT NEEDS TO BE MEASURED? THE VITAL SIGNS

When doctors want to get a quick idea of how a patient is doing, they take the patient's "vital signs," including pulse, temperature, and blood pressure. Knowing the normal range of these measures for a healthy person, the doctor can quickly assess the patient's overall health. The goal of monitoring vital signs of natural resources is much the same: to learn about overall ecosystem health by measuring key features. Experts can be brought together to determine what

must be measured in a community (aspects of plants, animals, water, etc.) and how. With the results of the monitoring, managers can know how a community is doing currently and over time, and be warned if something is happening outside the normal range of variation for that system.

What is the normal range of variation? That question is easier to answer for human health than for most natural systems, because human health has been closely studied for a long time. Only by repeatedly measuring the same aspects of a natural system can we attempt to learn what is normal, or "healthy." One might measure the number of young birds successfully

---

ORCUTT'S SPINEFLOWER

A tiny, prickly plant called Orcutt's spineflower is known at only two locations in the United States—both are in San Diego County and one is within the Point Loma Ecological Reserve. The spineflowers on Point Loma are much more protected from disturbance than those growing at the other site, so this population, the larger of the two, is extremely important.

The 1993 edition of *Jepson's Manual of Higher Plants of California*, a botanical bible of sorts, lists the plant as "ENDANGERED CA, PRESUMED EXTINCT. Coastal scrub; 60-125m. s Sco (Del Mar to Point Loma, San Diego Co.). Last known habitat has been developed."

The Navy has been working with Dr. Ellen Bauder of San Diego State University and the U.S. Fish and Wildlife Service to learn basic information about this plant and how to propagate it.

---

reared per nest, the number of plant species in a transect, or the level of dissolved oxygen in a body of water. Only long-term data can reveal which trends are reversible and which are not.

Increasingly, biological inventory and monitoring work is being done on Point Loma: studies on breeding birds (nesting heron colonies, peregrine falcons), the rocky intertidal ecosystem, the kelp beds, terrestrial vegetation, rare plants, air quality, water quality, terrestrial invertebrates, reptiles and amphibians, small mammals, large carnivores, and soils. This exciting and rewarding work has revealed that Point Loma has much more to offer than the previously noted "relatively few forms of wildlife." The National Park Service, the Navy, and the city of San Diego are working with many partners to understand the ecological condition, importance, and management of this biologically complex place. Partners include government agencies, universities, colleges, high schools, museums, private nonprofit organizations, biological consultants, and volunteers.

To date, we know that more than a thousand species call Point Loma home, and that does not include what swims in the kelp beds. By a conservative estimate, the current species lists include more than 300 species of terrestrial plants (versus the old list of 30), 52 lichens, 170 marine plants and animals, 20 mammals, more than 250 birds (versus the old list of 65), 20 reptiles and amphibians, and 298 terrestrial invertebrate species. A new discovery, a large spider in the genus *Apostichus*, may occur here and nowhere else in the world.

And with more inventories to come, who knows how many species will be added to science? In stark contrast to 1973, the park's 1996 General Management Plan and Environmental Impact Statement says that "the USFWS considers Point Loma to be a major wildlife resource of regional significance due to the quality, abundance, and diversity of habitats and its position adjacent to the Pacific Ocean."

Not all the news revealed by these inventory and monitoring projects is good. Nineteen species of reptiles and amphibians lived here seventy years ago; now there are just over a dozen. Black abalone used to be stacked on top of each other in the intertidal zone. Now they are gone. California gnatcatchers once bred on Point Loma, now they do not. Some of the news, however, is exciting. The silvery legless lizards (*Aniella pulchra*) still survive here, as does a population of an endangered plant,

Black abalone, once thick in the intertidal zone, are now gone from Point Loma.

Orcutt's spineflower *(Chorizanthe orcuttiana)*. Botanists describe the "old growth" coastal sage scrub community as unique and impressively pristine. And with the multiagency efforts to remove exotic species, the situation is improving all the time.

The important point is that more and more information is being gathered and used to learn about and care for this complex and beautiful place. And the list of resources inventoried and monitored keeps growing. Cabrillo National Monument now has an entire division dedicated to natural resource science, unusual for a "cultural" park. Learning how a reserve functions biologically is the key to knowing how to keep it healthy. Even when research does not answer specific management questions, it can go a long way toward clarifying how biological systems work, and these stories can be shared with the public, so people can learn about, be inspired by, and care for this surprisingly complex, interesting place.

LEARNING TO LOVE LIGHTLY

Parks are for people, insofar as parks can be enjoyed "unimpaired." Visitor education and inspiration are central to park management, while protecting the resources is also critical to the park mission. Resource studies without education and enforcement would probably end up recording the steady demise of species, with little hope of recovery. Education helps inform the public, young and old, about their natural heritage. Whether this comes from speaking with a ranger or volunteer, reading a wayside exhibit, watching a movie, or just picking up a species list, educational information can make park visits more interesting and memorable. Increased understanding often leads to increased appreciation. The more a visitor understands about a natural area's unique qualities, the more likely he or she is to care about and for them.

About 160 to a few hundred acres of natural land (depending upon categories and tide level) are open to the public at

Point Loma. Most of that is in Cabrillo National Monument.
Each year more than one million visitors come; given that vol-
ume, and the rarity and vulnerability of the resources, public
cooperation is indispensable.

Strict preservation laws are in effect at Cabrillo, and fortunately most people do "take only pictures, leave only foot-
prints," enjoying but not measurably impacting the natural
beauty of Point Loma. Some people sense this ethic, but still
act on impulse, when they
carve initials into sand-
stone cliffs or take a hermit
crab home in the car. A tiny
minority willfully disregard
the rules—for example,
poaching from parks for
their own economic gain,
glory, or entertainment.
Many who do fall outside
the law are completely
unaware of what a national
park means, or that things
growing, living, or simply existing here are not up for grabs.
These natural resources belong to *all* the citizens of the United
States, therefore everything must be left alone, unimpaired, for
each and every subsequent visitor to enjoy.

*Visitor educa-
tion is vital
to the protec-
tion of natural
resources at
Point Loma.*

BEING THERE

Every day Cabrillo National Monument park rangers and volunteers talk to school children, senior citizens, and other visitors
about the natural and cultural resources of Point Loma. Rangers
patrol the entire park, keeping an eye out for any inappropriate
behavior and to interact with, protect, and educate the public.
Uniformed volunteers working in the tidepool area have noticed
that some rambunctious visitors become much better behaved

once a ranger strides through the area. Signs help, but it has been shown that the most effective deterrent to misbehavior is having a park ranger there in person. Nearly anyone working on Point Loma in uniform will be asked questions. It doesn't matter if that uniform says National Park Service, U.S. Navy, U.S. Coast Guard, City of San Diego, Fort Rosecrans National Cemetery, or Cabrillo National Monument Foundation. All help visitors appreciate and enjoy what Point Loma has to offer.

The Navy has been actively engaged in public education for years. Their staff has constructed wayside exhibits along Highway 209, created and distributed brochures on the plants and wildlife of Point Loma, and given many presentations to the public about their natural resource programs. The Navy also founded the Fort Guijarros Historical Museum, which is dedicated to researching and interpreting the archaeology and natural history of Ballast Point.

The City of San Diego has funded monitoring of the Point Loma kelp beds and water quality for decades. Through cooperation with the Scripps Institution of Oceanography, the city has helped to discover a great deal about the kelp beds and their dynamics. Research by the late Dr. Mia Tegner of Scripps demonstrated that the treated effluent piped into the ocean off Point Loma's shore has not negatively impacted the kelp beds in a significant way, but that overharvesting of marine mammals and fish may have. Along the way, Dr. Tegner and her colleagues discovered a great deal more about ecosystem dynamics and the influence of global weather patterns on the kelp beds.

UNITED WE STAND

The global importance of some of Point Loma's habitats became very clear at the end of the twentieth century. In response, the 640-acre Point Loma Ecological Reserve was created in 1995. The Navy had been planning to develop areas of Point Loma when the U.S. Fish and Wildlife Service stepped in. The Fish

A LESSON IN RESERVE ECOLOGY

Today Point Loma is an ecological "island" amid a sea of development. Though Point Loma and other patches of open land are valuable, important habitat for plants and animals, they are changed by what is happening in and around them. Not only do species or populations get lost during habitat destruction and isolation, new ones are added. The centuries-old roles that fire and flood once played are changed. Fire-dependent species can be predicted to die off if all wildfire is suppressed. Even if all development, pollution, or even visitation is halted, the reserve will continue to evolve in isolation.

Many factors contribute to the changes a reserve undergoes. Some populations of plants or animals can only survive by receiving new individuals from outside the reserve boundary. Some species have requirements, such as a fresh water source, that are only met outside the reserve. If the area outside the reserve is developed those species either leave or die out. Large carnivores often require large expanses of land to survive. Comparing reptile and amphibian species on large and small reserves, scientists found that on Point Loma and elsewhere in southern California the first species to fall and become extirpated are those which require large areas of habitat.

Two goals for reserves are to reduce native species loss, limiting or reversing negative human impact to the natural ecosystems; and to restore land and natural processes as close as possible to original biological richness.

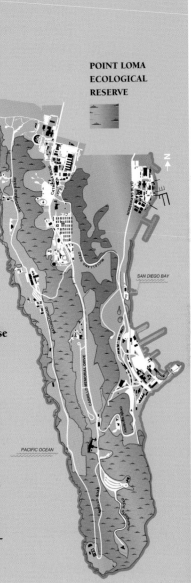

POINT LOMA
ECOLOGICAL
RESERVE

SAN DIEGO BAY

PACIFIC OCEAN

and Wildlife Service, which manages threatened and endangered species populations in the United States, discussed the cumulative impact that separate development actions would have on the increasingly rare Point Loma habitats. The agency proposed that the most efficient way for the Navy to go forward and avoid lengthy and expensive compliance procedures was to establish a nature preserve on Point Loma.

Don Lydy, Chief of Facilities, Naval Command, Control and Ocean Surveillance Center, RDT&E Division, now known as Space and Naval Warfare Systems Center, San Diego, at the time led the effort to create what has become the Point Loma Ecological Reserve. The Reserve is co-managed by the National Park Service and the Navy, and its progress is overseen by a working group consisting of all Point Loma landowners and the U.S. Fish and Wildlife Service. Communication among agencies across the peninsula has been enhanced, and Reserve management has improved. In light of this new perspective, research originally slated to occur only at Cabrillo or only on Navy land has often been expanded to include the Reserve. Conservation

LOCALS ONLY

Landscaping your yard with native plants has a host of benefits. It attracts local native wildlife and makes your yard and neighborhood more interesting. Gardening costs will go down because native plants are naturally adapted to the local weather, requiring little to no watering once they are established.

Also, the plants have evolved with native insects, and so have natural defenses and suffer less disease. That means you can stop buying harmful and polluting insecticides and herbicides. Replacing that exotic, water-wasting lawn with native

habitat will bring birds flocking to your yard. It will reduce the spread of non-native species and increase native biodiversity.

efforts, too, have extended across bureaucratic boundaries, particularly in the area of vegetation management. All this progress is largely due to the Point Loma Ecological Reserve, which has allowed managers from separate and very different agencies to think holistically.

VEGETATION MANAGEMENT: THE GOOD, THE BAD, AND THE INVASIVE

To preserve species you must preserve their habitat, that is the first rule of preservation, whether the concern is for plants, animals, or other natural resources. Some nonnative plant species can displace native species, growing up and over stretches of wild coastal bluff scrub. For example, after enough time, what remains is a wide, homogenous swath of a few nonnative species, hosting a depauperate plant and animal community. Nonnative plants were introduced to Point Loma in many different ways, but among the most active human participants were the Army, the Navy, and even the National Park Service. Efforts are now under way to try to reverse this practice. Cabrillo National Monument and the Navy have since joined forces to contain and remove these plants from all natural areas of the Point Loma Ecological Reserve.

In the 1980s, NPS staff started clearing nonnative plants and in the 1990s, the first foray was made into tag-team weed pulling. Expanding nonnative vegetation removal efforts beyond the park boundaries was a big leap forward. This was only possible through cooperation among Point Loma neighbors, including the U.S. Navy, Fort Rosecrans National Cemetery, the U.S. Coast Guard, and the Point Loma Wastewater Treatment Plant. A pivotal change has occurred through the expansion of the Youth Conservation Corps (YCC) program.

From a single student hired for one summer, the YCC program at Cabrillo National Monument has expanded to a large group of high school students, several site supervisors (often

Youth Conservation Corps workers remove nonnative plants.

former YCC kids), and various vans and a truck for moving the students, equipment, and excised exotic vegetation all over Point Loma. These YCC participants remove great piles of nonnative vegetation from Point Loma each summer. The Navy helped expand the program, and in return for that support, YCC students began removing exotic vegetation from Navy-owned natural areas all over Point Loma, not just in Cabrillo National Monument. Clearly, this Reserve-wide method is the way to get things done.

Another aspect of the YCC program has blossomed—an environmental education program. Each Friday during their summer tenure here, the students get a day off from pulling weeds to learn about conservation issues through guest lectures and field trips to San Diego parks and reserves. The goal is to foster an environmental ethic among the youth. The YCC has inspired hundreds of young people to care for the natural world. Even a former director of the National Park Service, Robert Stanton, got his start as a YCC "kid" years ago.

ROSE IS A ROSE IS A ROSE — UNLESS IT'S NONNATIVE

Complementary grassroots efforts sprang up at Point Loma during the 1990s. The Navy, led again by Don Lydy, began a progressive movement to remove nonnative species from its landscaped areas and use native plants instead. Navy employees supplied the labor, volunteering for this physically demanding work during their free time.

Fort Rosecrans National Cemetery, historic resting place for tens of thousands of war veterans and their families, a bastion of beautiful, but exotic, trees and shrubs and well known as a great birding place, is changing too. Portions of the landscaping along the Highway 209 corridor have been converted from non-native to native plants. Because vehicles are effective movers of nonnative seeds, fewer nonnative plants along the highway reduces exotic species spread. This change made in the cemetery landscaping is an important step and another contribution to the collective effort to slow exotic species encroachment into the Point Loma Ecological Reserve.

DON'T PICK UP HITCHHIKERS

Imagine trying to stem the tide of nonnative seeds pouring into Cabrillo National Monument. These seeds arrive daily by the hundreds, transported on vehicle tires and undercarriages, hiking boots and socks, birds, mammals, wind, and water. The more nonnative species growing outside the park, the more work it takes to stop them from increasing their hold and to expand native habitat. Before and after you visit a park or other natural open space, dispose of all visible seeds stuck to your socks, boots, clothes, tires, and car. This will go a long way toward keeping the outdoors native, wild, diverse, and beautiful.

GIVE ME THE DIRT

Cabrillo National Monument, the Point Loma Wastewater Treatment Plant, and Fort Rosecrans National Cemetery have been swapping dirt for years. Why? Every clod of dirt from native habitat may contain seeds of native plants. If used to revegetate a disturbed or denuded area, this dirt may well yield some volunteer native plants free of charge. The corollary is true for dirt from a highly disturbed site with nonnative plants. Use nonnative dirt to revegetate an area, and nonnative plants spring forth, creating lots of work and threatening the local ecosystem. Even native seeds that are not specifically from Point Loma plants can cause problems. Nonlocal seeds can germinate and cross breed with Point Loma plants, changing genetic stock that might be unique in the world. So when it comes to dirt, Point Lomans try to keep it local and keep it clean.

Whether it is pulling weeds, patrolling, finding funding for projects, studying herons, educating the public, selling books at the bookstore, or attending Reserve meetings, every action is a part of the big picture. Through the combined effort of many different agencies, universities, organizations, and individuals and continuing public support and cooperation, we have hope of achieving the mission of the National Park Service: to restore and preserve this beautiful, complicated fragment of southern California's natural world "unimpaired for the enjoyment of future generations."

REFERENCES/ADDITIONAL READING

National Park Service. 1996. *General Management Plan, Final Environmental Impact Statement for Cabrillo National Monument, California.* U.S. Department of Interior. 233 pp.

National Park Service, 1976. *Master Plan for Cabrillo National Monument, California.* U.S. Department of Interior, Western Regional Office. 51pp.

Zedler, Joy b. 1976. *Ecological Resource Inventory of the Cabrillo National Monument Intertidal Zone.* Biology Department, San Diego State University, Project Report prepared for the U.S. Department of Interior, National Park Service. 64pp.

Hickman, James C. ed. 1993. *The Jepson Manual: Higher Plants of California.* University of California Press, Berkeley. 140pp.

INDEX

A

Abalone, 9, 74, 75-76, 79, 134, 148, 155, 165
Abronia maritima, 94, 99
Acacia (*Acacia spp.*), 109, 153
Accessibility demands, 77, 166-167
Acorn barnacle (*Balanus glandula, Chthamalus spp.*), 62
Adaptive processes, 66
  direct development, 121
  kelp forests, 70-72
  nutrient limitations and, 69, 71-72
  rocky intertidal habitat, 67-70
  semiterrestrial conditions and, 67-68
  space limitations and, 68-69
  sunlight requirements and, 70, 71
  tail-loss strategy, 121
  territorial defense, 69
  wave action stress and, 68, 71
  See also Mediterranean plant communities; Plant communities
Adenostoma fasciculatum, 88, 94, 98
Aeolian deposits, 22-23
Agave shawii, 101, 102, 115
Aggregating anemone (*Anthopleura elegantissima*), 9, 67, 69
Air pollution, 104, 105, 106
Algae:
  algal turfs, 62, 65, 67, 77
  drift algae, 65
  rockweed, 62
  upper intertidal zone and, 62
  See also Kelp forest
Alligator lizard (*Elgaria multicarinata*), 121-122, 130
Ambrosia bipinnatifida, 94
Ambrosia chamissonis, 99
American oystercatcher (*Haematopus palliatus*), 117
Amphibians, 120, 125, 130-131
Amsinckia menziesii, 88
Anemones, 9, 67, 69
Aniella pulchra, 125, 165

Animal populations, 9, 10, 109
  birds, 116-118, 124, 129, 161
  breeding rookeries and, 117
  disease and, 117-118
  extinctions/restorations and, 126-129
  habitat fragmentation/edge effects and, 128, 129-130
  habitat loss and, 105-106, 112
  invertebrates, 118-120, 125-126
  mammals, 114-116, 128-129
  native species, 114-124
  nonnative exotics, 124-126
  nutritional deficiencies and, 117-118
  organic sediment and, 15
  poaching/collection and, 130-131
  predation, 112, 116, 124
  recreational hunting and, 126
  reproductive failure and, 118
  reptiles/amphibians, 120-124, 125, 127-128
  urbanization and, 112, 124
  weed invasion and, 107-109
  See also Marine systems
Anniella pulchra, 122
Anthopleura elegantissima, 9, 67, 69
Antilocapra americana, 114, 128
Aphanisma (*Aphanisma blitoides*), 102
Aplysia californica, 69
Aptostichus, 119, 165
Ardea herodias, 117
Argentine ant (*Linepithema humile*), 125, 127, 154
Arizona elegans, 125, 127
Armadillidium vulgare, 125
Artemisia californica, 88, 89, 94, 95
Aspidoscelis hyperythrus, 122, 125
Australian eucalyptus (*Eucalyptus spp.*), 109, 117

B

Badger (*Taxidea taxus*), 114, 129, 136
Baja California, 50, 57, 76, 80, 92, 129
Balanophyllia elegans, 19
Balanus glandula, 62
Ballast Point, 127, 129, 134-136, 142, 147, 150, 168

Barnacles, 62, 68
Barrel cactus (*Ferocactus viridescens*), 97, 102
Batrachoseps major, 121, 125
Bats, 115
Bayside Trail, 15, 16, 114, 115
Beach burrweed (*Ambrosia chamissonis*), 99
Beaches:
  ancient beaches, 17-18
  beach ridges, 22, 26
  climatic conditions and, 34
  foredune scrub and, 98-99
  pocket beaches, 27, 49
  wave action and, 49
  See also Sea cliffs
Beach evening primrose (*Camissonia cheiranthifolia*), 99
Beach ridges, 22, 26
Beetles, 119
Bergerocactus emoryi, 97, 102
Bird Rock terrace, 16, 17, 19, 20, 25
Birds, 116-118, 124, 129, 136, 161
Black abalone (*Haliotis cracherodii*), 9, 75, 134, 165
Black-crowned night heron (*Nycticorax nycticorax*), 117
Black oystercatcher (*Haematopus bachmani*), 117
Black sage (*Salvia mellifera*), 88, 94, 96
Black-tailed jackrabbit (*Lepus californicus bennettii*), 114, 129, 139
Blue-belly lizard, 122-123
Bluffs. *See* Sand dunes; Sea cliffs
Boa kelp. *See* Feather boa kelp
Bobcat, 114, 128
Boxthorn (*Lycium californicum*), 95, 99
Brant's cormorant (*Phalacrocorax penicillatus*), 117
Broad-winged hawk (*Buteo platypterus*), 117
Buckthorn, 91
Bufo loreas, 120
Buteo jamaicensis, 117
Buteo platypterus, 117

C

Cabrillo, Juan Rodríguez, 54, 139, 140, 142, 153, 158

Cabrillo National Monument, 57, 61, 76, 84, 108, 153, 155-156, 158

Cactus, 95, 97, 102

California buckwheat (*Eriogonum fasciculatum*), 94, 95, 96

California chaparral, 98, 103

California encelia (*Encelia californica*), 94, 96

California glossy snake (*Arizona elegans*), 125, 127

California gnatcatcher, 106, 165

California king snake, 125, 130

California legless lizard (*Anniella pulchra*), 122

California mouse (*Peromyscus californicus*), 115

California mussel (*Mytilus californianus*), 62, 67, 69, 76

California Natural Diversity Database, 101, 156

California sagebrush (*Artemisia californica*), 88, 89, 94, 95

California sea hare (*Aplysia californica*), 69

California State Water Resources Control Board, 56

Camissonia cheiranthifolia, 94, 99

Cancer spp., 60

Canis latrans, 114, 115, 120, 126

Canyon ecosystems, 10

Carpet-weed (*Carpobrotus edulis*), 109, 127, 153, 154

Carpobrotus edulis, 109, 127, 153, 154

Catalina Eddy, 34-35

Cattle industries, 143-145

Ceanothus verrucosus, 88, 94, 98, 102, 103

Cemetery. *See* Fort Rosecrans National Cemetery

Census reports, 148, 152

Chamise (*Adenostoma fasciculatum*), 88, 94, 98

Channel Islands, 50

Chaparral, 86, 89-90, 92, 94, 95, 98, 103

Charina trivirgata, 125, 126

Cheatodipus fallax, 115

Chinese population, 148

Chitons, 58, 62, 68, 136

Choeronycteris mexicana, 115

Cholla, 97, 102

Chorizanthe orcuttiana, 9, 101,
107, 164, 166

Chthamalus spp., 62

City of San Diego, 11, 57
ecological management and, 165
founding/development of, 54-56
marine terraces and, 19
population figures, 132, 148, 152, 154

City of San Diego Wastewater Department, 9

Clams, 136

Clean Water Act, 77

Cliffs. *See* Sea cliffs

Cliff spurge (*Euphorbia misera*), 88, 94, 96, 99, 102

Climatic conditions, 30
Catalina Eddy, 34-35
El Niño/La Niña, 41-43, 44, 73-74, 117
June gloom/stratus season conditions, 34
marine habitats and, 73-74
Pacific decadal oscillation, 43-44
Pacific high/desert trough and, 33, 34, 36
Point Loma conditions, 33, 135
Santa Ana winds, 37-38
storm front movement, 38-40
summer weather, 33-35
variability of, 30-33
winter weather, 35-43
See also Mediterranean plant communities; Oceanography

Cnemotettix miniatus, 119

Cneoridium dumosum, 89

Coastal bluff scrub, 98, 99, 100

Coastal cholla (*Opuntia prolifera*), 97

Coastal rosy boa (*Charina trivirgata*), 125, 126

Coastal sage succulent scrub, 9, 94, 95-98, 100, 103, 166

Coastal scrub oak (*Quercus dumosa*), 94, 98, 102, 135, 142

Coast horned lizard (*Phrynosoma coronatum*), 127, 130-131

Coast wall flower (*Erysimum ammophilum*), 102

Coast woolly-head (*Nemacaulis
denudata* var. *denudata*), 102

Collecting, 76-77, 130-131, 167

Colluvial deposits, 23

Coluber constrictor, 125, 127

Commercial enterprise:
abalone harvest, 75, 148
barnacle glue and, 68
fisheries, 60, 79-81, 155
hide/tallow industry, 144-145
kelp harvesting, 58-60
limitations on, 155-156
livestock/agriculture, 143-144
river re-routing and, 149
sea otter pelt trade, 146-147
whaling industry, 147, 149

Conglomerates, 14, 16

Conservation efforts, 8, 11
accessibility demands and, 77, 166-167
artificial nesting sites, 117
domestic pet release and, 124-125, 126
ecological monitoring, 81
extinction/restoration and, 126-129
habitat fragmentation/edge effects and, 106-107, 129-130
marine reserve establishment, 81-82
native vegetation, contiguous parcels of, 93
Pacific gray whales, 80
plant communities and, 104-109
poaching/collecting threat and, 76-77, 130-131
preservation laws, 167
reserve size limitation/isolation and, 104-106
sea cliff erosion, 25, 27, 75-76
stages in, 9
weed invasion and, 107-109
See also Ecological threats; Human impact; Management

Corals, 19, 20

Coreopsis maritima, 101, 102

Cormorants, 117

Coronado Island, 52, 152

Costansó, Miguel, 140

Coves, 27

Coyotes (*Canis latrans*), 114, 115, 120, 126

Crabs, 62, 136

Cretaceous period, 12
  fault activity and, 16-17
  gravel deposits, 14, 16
  inner-fan valley conglomer-
    ates, 14
  mid-fan channels, 14-15
  organic sediment, 15
  sediment deposition, 15-16
  submarine fan formation,
    12-14, 15-16
  syncline feature, 16-17
  See also Geologic history;
    Quaternary period
Crotalus oreganus, 9, 123-124,
  125
Crotalus ruber, 123, 125, 127
Crotalus viridis helleri, 161
Cryptantha (Cryptantha intermedia), 88

D
Dana, Richard Henry, 140-141,
  144, 145
Davidson, Winifred, 139, 141,
  143
DDT, 118
Deer, 114, 128, 136, 152
Degradation. See Conservation;
  Ecological threats;
  Management
Department of Veterans Affairs,
  9, 11
Desert cottontail, 114
Desert king snake, 125
Desert shrew (Notiosorex craw-
  fordi), 114, 115
Development pressures, 10, 98,
  99, 101, 102, 106, 112, 124,
  152
Disease:
  bacterial epidemics, 75
  pollution and, 77-78
  species decline and, 76
  yellow fat disease (steatites),
    117-118
Distichlis spicata, 94, 99
Dudleya (Dudleya lanceolata, D.
  edulis), 86, 94, 97
Duhaut-Cilly, August, 138-139
Dust particles, 22-23

E
Earthquake activity, 21
Ecological threats, 75
  abalone declines, 75-76

algal turf, invertebrate popu-
    lations and, 77
  bay-flushing pollution, 78
California mussel and, 76
  fisheries management and,
    78-81
  habitat fragmentation/edge
    effects, 106-107, 112, 128,
    129-130
  island biogeography theory
    and, 104-105
  plant communities and, 99-
    101, 104-109
  poaching/collecting and, 76-
    77, 130-131, 167
  recolonization failure, 105
  recreational hunting and,
    126, 152
  reproduction, interference
    with, 77, 78-79
  riprap deposits, 75-76
  run-off pollution, 78
  sea otter populations, 146-147
  sea star populations, 76
  sea urchin populations, 79-
    81, 154-155
  sewage pollution, 77-78, 81
  species saturation, 105
  urban development, 98, 99,
    101, 102, 106, 112, 126,
    152
  weed invasion, 107-109
  See also Conservation
    efforts; Human impact;
    Management
Ecosystem health.
  See Conservation efforts;
    Ecological threats;
    Management
Edge effects, 106-107, 129-130
Education programs, 9, 11, 131,
  166, 167-168, 172
Egregia menziesii, 64, 68
Eisenia arborea, 64-65
Eleodes, 119
Elgaria multicarinata, 121
El Niño/La Niña, 41-43, 44, 73-
  74, 117
Encelia californica, 94, 96
Endangered species, 99-102,
  118
Endangered Species Act, 101
Enhydra lutris, 79, 136, 146-147,
  155
Eriogonum fasciculatum, 94, 95, 96

Erosion, 12
  colluvial deposits and, 23
  photographic comparisons,
    25, 27
  sea cliff erosion, 25-27
  storm surge/tidal effects, 49
  tidepools and, 25
  wave action and, 49
  See also Marine terraces
Erysimum ammophilum, 102
Eschrichtius robustus, 57, 80,
  147-148
Eucalyptus spp., 109, 117
Euphorbia misera, 88, 94, 96,
  99, 102
European earwig (Forficula
  auricularia), 125
European explorers, 137-142
Evening primrose (Camissonia
  cheiranthifolia), 99
Evolutionary pressures. See
  Adaptive processes
Exotics, 9, 112, 124-126, 127,
  153, 171-173
Extinctions, 102, 126-129, 132-
  133, 164

F
Falco peregrinus, 118
Fault activity, 16-17, 20-22
Feather boa kelp (Egregia men-
  ziesii), 64, 68
Felis domesticus, 126
Feral cats, 126
Ferocactus viridescens, 97, 102
Fiddleneck (Amsinckia menzie-
  sii), 88
Fire incidence:
  annuals/fire-followers and,
    91
  history of, 103
  plant communities and,
    89-91
  seeders and, 90-91
  sprouters and, 89-90, 97
Fisheries, 60, 78-81, 155
Fish-hook cactus (Mammalaria
  dioica), 97
Fog, 34, 35
Food acquisition, 42, 69, 71-72,
  73, 112
Foredune scrub, 98-99, 100
Forficula auricularia, 125
Fort Guijarros, 145-146
Fort Guijarros Historical

Museum, 168
Fort Rosecrans, 150-152, 154
Fort Rosecrans National
    Cemetery, 151, 154, 171,
    172-173
Fossils:
    corals, 19
    marine terraces and, 17, 19
    trace fossils, 15
Foxes, 114, 128-129

G

Garden slender salamander
    (*Batrachoseps major*), 121, 125
General Management Plan
    and Environmental Impact
    Statement, 165
Geococcyx californianus, 129, 139
Geologic history, 12
    aeolian deposits, 22-23
    beach ridges, 22
    colluvial deposits, 23
    compression forces, 16
    Cretaceous period, 12-17
    fault activity, 16-17, 20-22
    glacial periods, 18-19
    marine terraces, 17-19
    mid-fan channels, 14-15
    Quaternary period, 17-28
    sea cliff erosion, 25-27
    sea level variations, 18-19
    submarine fan formation,
        12-14, 15-16
    syncline feature, 16-17
    uplift activity, 17, 20-22
Giant kelp (*Macrocystis pyrifera*),
    58, 59, 65, 70-71, 77
Girella nigricans, 72
Glacial history, 18-19
Global warming, 20, 45, 74
Glowworm (*Zarhipis spp.*), 119
Goldenbush (*Isocoma mensiesii*),
    94, 99
Golden-spined cereus
    (*Bergerocactus emoryi*), 97, 102
Gravel deposits, 14, 16
Gray fox (*Urocyon cineroargen-
    teus*), 9, 114, 115
Great blue heron (*Ardea hero-
    dias*), 117
Greater roadrunner (*Geococcyx
    californianus*), 129, 139
Green abalone (*Haliotis fulgens*),
    75-76
Grosbeak, 116

H

Habitat fragmentation, 106-
    107, 112, 128, 129-130, 150
Habitat health. *See* Conservation
    efforts; Ecological threats;
    Management
Habitat loss, 98, 99, 101, 102,
    106, 109
Haematopus bachmani, 117
Halibut (*Paralichthys californi-
    cus*), 60
Haliotis crachervdii, 9, 75, 134,
    165
Haliotis fulgens, 75-76
Haliotis sorenseni, 79, 148
Hard chaparral species, 86,
    91, 95
Haumatopus palliatus, 117
Hawks, 116-117
Helmenthoglipta spp., 120
Herbicides, 109
Herons, 117-118
Heteromeles arbutifolia, 87, 88,
    94, 98, 142
Holly-leaved cherry (*Prunus
    ilicifolia*), 103
Horned lizard toad (*Phrynosoma
    coronatum*), 127
Horsehair worm, 120
House cat (*Felis domesticus*), 126
Human impact, 11, 132
    animal releases, 116, 124-
        125, 126
    construction projects, 149,
        150, 151, 152, 155
    ecological threat of, 56, 75, 76
    European explorers, 137-142
    habitat fragmentation/edge
        effects, 106-107, 112, 128,
        129-130, 150
    indigenous population, 134-
        139, 143, 145, 148, 151
    irrigated landscapes, 127
    light pollution, 128
    pesticide use, 78, 118
    prehistoric populations, 132-
        136
    river re-routing/channel clear-
        ing, 149, 150-151, 152, 155
    road-building and, 130, 150,
        152
    sea otter populations and,
        146-147
    sewage discharge, 77-78, 81,
        154-155

shell middens and, 134, 136
    Spanish rule/mission era,
        142-143
    trail systems, 139
    urban development, 10, 98,
        99, 101, 102, 106, 112,
        124, 152
    vegetation history and, 102-
        103
    visitor traffic, 77, 155-156,
        166-167
    See also Commercial enter-
        prise; Conservation efforts;
        Management; Military
        activity
Hurricanes, 50-51
Hyla regilla, 120

I

Imperial Beach, 22
Industry. *See* Commercial enter-
    prise
Insects, 119-120, 125-126, 127
International Whaling
    Commission, 80
Intertidal habitat. *See* Rocky
    intertidal habitat
Intertidal kelps, 64-65
Intertidal sage scrub, 9
Invasive species. *See* Exotics
Invertebrates, 15, 62, 77, 118-
    120, 125-126
Iron pisoliths, 23, 24
Island biogeography theory,
    104-106
Isocoma menziesii, 94, 99

J

Jackrabbit (*Lepus californicus
    bennettii*), 114, 129, 139
Jerusalem cricket (*Stenopelmatus
    spp.*), 120
Joyce, Barry, 146
June gloom, 34

K

Kearny Mesa, 128
Kelletia kelletii, 72
Kellet's whelk (*Kelletia kelletii*),
    72
Kelp bass (*Paralabrax clathra-
    tus*), 74
Kelp forests, 42, 44, 52, 57
    adaptive processes in, 70-72
    algal turfs and, 65

climatic effects and, 73-74
commercial harvesting of,
   58-60
dispersal systems in, 73
diversity/productivity of,
   60-61
ecological threats to, 77-79,
   154-155
fishery activity in, 60
giant kelp, 58, 59
growth conditions, 72
holdfasts, 60, 71
intertidal kelps, 64-65, 72
keyed illustration of, 64
microhabitats within, 60-
   61, 74
nutrient limitations and, 42,
   71-72, 73
sea urchins and, 65, 79-81,
   154-155
subtidal location of, 58
sunlight requirements and,
   70, 71, 77
understory kelps, 71
wave action and, 71
zonation and, 65
Kelps, 64-65, 68, 71, 72, 74
Kit fox (Vulpes macrotis macrotis), 114, 128-129, 136
Knobby star (Pisaster giganteus),
   72
Kumeyaay Indians, 137-139,
   143, 145, 148, 151

L
La Jolla, 16, 21, 47, 76, 117
Laminaria farlowii, 65, 71
Landsliding, 21, 23
La Niña, 41-43, 73-74
La Playa, 139, 149, 150
Lemonadeberry (Rhus integrifo-
   lia), 87, 88, 94, 97, 142
Lepus californicus bennettii, 114,
   129, 139
Lichens, 105, 106
Light pollution, 128
Limpets, 62, 67, 69, 76-77, 117
Linda Vista Terrace, 17
Lined shore crab (Pachygrapsus
   crassipes), 62
Linepitherma humile, 125, 127,
   154
Littorina spp., 62
Live-forever (Dudleya lanceolata,
   D. edulis), 97

Lizards, 121-123, 125, 127, 130
Lobsters, 60, 72, 78, 79
Lottia gigantea, 69, 76-77
Lotus nuttallianus, 102
Lycium californicum, 95, 99

M
Macrocystis pyrifera, 58, 59, 65,
   70-71, 77
Malosma laurina, 94
Mammalaria dioica, 97
Mammal population, 114-115,
   128-129, 136
Management:
   early history of, 158-161
   ecological reserve develop-
      ment, 168-171
   environmental awareness
      and, 160-161
   kelp regeneration, 154-155
   native vegetation landscap-
      ing and, 170
   natural resource science and,
      166
   park rangers, roles of, 167-
      168
   people management and,
      166-167
   preservation laws, 167
   soil control, 173-174
   species inventories and, 162-
      163, 165
   vegetation management,
      171-173
   vital signs monitoring, 81,
      163-166, 168
Manzanita, 88
Marine sedimentary rocks,
   16-17
Marine systems, 56-57
   adaptive processes in, 67-72
   conservation efforts and,
      81-82
   disturbances of, 65-66
   ecological threats to, 75-81
   interactions of, 72-74
   kelp forests, 58-61, 70-72
   ocean climate effects on,
      73-74
   rocky intertidal area, 57-58,
      67-70
   zonation and, 61-66
Marine terraces, 17
   abrasion platforms and, 17, 22
   coral fossils, dating process

and, 19
fault zones and, 21, 22
glacial history and, 18-19
sand dunes and, 22
sea cliffs and, 17-18
sea level variations and, 18-19
topographic height and, 19,
   22
uplift/subsidence information
   and, 20-21
Maritime succulent scrub, 9
Masticophis flagellum, 125, 127
Masticophis lateralis, 124, 125
Mean Lower Low Water
   (MLLW) datum, 46
Mediterranean plant communities, 10, 84
   annual life history and, 87-
      88, 91
   aromatics, survival strategy
      of, 88-89
   convergent evolution and, 84
   drought-deciduous species,
      86, 95
   fire response in, 89-91, 97
   plant adaptations, 86-88
   plant community groupings,
      91-93
   seed invasion and, 108
   water loss minimization
      strategies, 87
   water storage strategies,
      86-87
   See also Native vegetation;
      Plant communities
Mephitis mephitis, 116
Mexican long-tongued bat
   (Choeronycteris mexicana), 115
Mexican settlers, 148
Mexicanthina lugubris, 69
Microseris douglasii ssp. platycarpha, 102
Migratory pathways:
   bird species, 116-117
   human migrations, 132-134
   Pacific gray whales, 57, 147-
      148
   vagrant traps and, 116
Military activity:
   current Point Loma installa-
      tion, 156
   Fort Guijarros, 145-146
   Fort Rosecrans, 150-152
   nonnative vegetation and,
      153, 171

preservation activities, 156
United States-Mexican war,
    148-149
World War II, 153-154
Mission Bay, 21, 78, 149, 155
Mission manzanita (*Xylococcus
    bicolor*), 88, 94, 98
Mission settlements, 142-143
Monitoring efforts, 81
    City of San Diego and, 168
    habitat vital signs, 163-166
    wildlife census, 165
    See also Management
Mountain lion (*Puma concolor*),
    113-114, 128, 136
Mt. Soledad, 17, 20, 21
Mule deer (*Odocoileus hemionus*),
    114, 128, 136, 152
Multi-bladed kelp (*Pterygophora
    californica*), 65, 71
Mussels, 62, 67, 69, 76, 117,
    136
Mytilus californianus, 62, 67,
    69, 76

N
National Climate Data Center,
    40
National Oceanic and
    Atmospheric Administration
    (NOAA), 56
National Park Service, 9, 11, 57,
    75, 153, 155, 156, 158, 165,
    170, 171
Native animal species, 112-114
    birds, 116-118
    invertebrates, 118-120
    mammals, 114-116
    reptiles/amphibians, 120-124
Native human populations,
    134-139, 143, 145, 148, 151
Native vegetation, 10, 93
    coastal bluff scrub, 98, 99
    coastal sage succulent scrub,
        95-98
    communities of, 94-95
    conservation efforts and, 104
    contiguous parcels, conserva-
        tion and, 93
    endangerment status of,
        99-101
    foredune scrub, 98-99
    forest growth, 139-141
    geographic features and,

102-103
    habitat fragmentation/edge
        effects and, 106-107
    southern maritime chapar-
        ral, 98
    weed invasion and, 107-109
    See also Mediterranean plant
        communities; Plant com-
        munities
Nearshore environment, 52
    human impact on, 56
    ocean climate and, 73-74
    See also Ecological threats;
        Marine systems; Rocky
        intertidal habitat
*Nemacaulis denudata var. denu-
    data*, 102
Neotoma, 115
Nestor Terrace, 17, 19, 20, 26
Nightshade (*Solanum xanti*), 88
Night snake, 125
Nonnative vegetation, 153, 156,
    171-173
North Island, 134-135, 152
Notiosorex crawfordi, 114, 115
Novara Street, 27
Nuttalina fluxa, 62
Nuttall's lotus (*Lotus nuttallia-
    nus*), 102
Nycticorax nycticorax, 117

O
Oaks, 94, 98, 102, 135, 142
Ocean Beach, 76, 151
Oceanography, 44-45
    climatic influence and, 30,
        33, 40-41, 44
    island sheltering effects,
        52, 73
    longshore currents, 49
    Pacific decadal oscillation,
        43-44
    sea level variations, 45-49
    storm surges, 48-49
    tidal action, 46-48
    water temperatures, 41-42
    wave action, 49-52
    wind motion and, 33, 50-51
Ochre sea star (*Pisaster ochra-
    ceus*), 9, 76
Octopus (*Octopus bimaculoides*),
    68
Odocoileus hemionus, 114, 128,
    136, 152

Opaleye (*Girella nigricans*), 72
Opuntia littoralis, 94
Opuntia prolifera, 97
Orange-crowned warbler
    (*Vermivora celata*), 118
Orange-throated whiptail
    (*Aspidoscelis hyperythrus*), 122,
    125
Orcutt's spineflower
    (*Chorizanthe orcuttiana*), 9,
    101, 107, 164, 166
Orobanche parishii ssp. brachyloba,
    102
Otters, 79, 136, 146-147, 155
Owl limpet (*Lottia gigantea*), 69,
    76-77

P
Pachygrapsus crassipes, 62
Pacific decadal oscillation
    (PDO), 43-44
Pacific gray whale (*Eschrichtius
    robustus*), 57, 80, 147-148
Pacific rattlesnake (*Crotalus
    oreganus*), 9, 123-124, 125,
    161
Pacific treefrog (*Hyla regilla*),
    120
Panulirus interruptus, 60, 78,
    79, 155
Paralabrax clathratus, 74
Paralichthys californicus, 60
Parasites, 120
Peregrine falcon (*Falco peregri-
    nus*), 118
Periwinkle snail (*Littorina spp.*),
    62
Peromyscus californicus, 115
Pesticide use, 78, 118
Phalacrocorax penicillatus, 117
Pheucticus ludovicianus, 116
Phragmatopoma californica, 68
Phrynosoma coronatum, 127,
    130-131
Phyllospadix torreyi, 64, 72
Phytoplankton, 69
Pill bug (*Armadillidium vulgare*),
    125
Pisaster giganteus, 72
Pisaster ochraceus, 9, 76
Pituophis catenifer, 124, 125
Plant communities, 9, 93
    adaptations in, 86-88, 103
    cacti, 95, 97, 102

California chaparral, 98, 103
canopy expansion strategy, 103
coastal bluff scrub, 98, 99
coastal sage succulent scrub, 95-97, 103
colony size limitations/isolation and, 104-106
conservation challenges and, 104-109
endangerment status of, 99-101
fire incidence in, 89-91, 97, 103
foredune scrub, 98-99
forest growth, 139-141
groupings of, 91-93
habitat fragmentation/edge effects and, 106-107
history of, 102-103
lichens, 105, 106
management of, 171-173
microhabitats of, 68
native vegetation, 93-99, 156, 170
nonnative vegetation, 153, 156, 171-173
rare plant species, 101-102, 106
southern maritime chaparral, 98
See also Kelp forest; Mediterranean plant communities; Native vegetation
Pleistocene epoch, 24
Poaching threats, 76-77, 130-131, 167
Pocket mouse (*Cheatodipus fallax*), 115
Point Conception, 35, 50
Point Guijarros, 145
Point Loma Ecological Reserve, 9, 84, 109, 168-171
Point Loma Lighthouse, 34, 35, 149-150, 158, 160
Point Loma Wastewater Treatment Plant, 57, 77, 154-155, 171, 173
Poison oak (*Toxicodendron diversilobum*), 89
Polar ice caps, 20
Political interests, 148-149
Pollution:

lichen, indicator function of, 105, 106
light pollution, 128
pesticide use, 78, 118
sewage discharge, 77-78, 81, 154-155
Porcellio laevis, 125
Post Cemetery, 154
Portolá, Gaspar de, 140, 142
Prehistoric populations, 132-136
Preservation. *See* Conservation
Procyon lotor, 116, 136
Pronghorn (*Antilocapra americana*), 114, 128
Prothonotary warbler (*Protonotaria citrea*), 116
Protonotaria citrea, 116
Prunus ilicifolia, 103
Pterygophora californica, 65, 71
Public policy, 9
Puma concolor, 113-114, 128, 136
Purple nightshade (*Solanum xanti*), 88
Purple sea urchin (*Strongylocentrotus purpuratus*), 72, 79

Q
Quaternary period, 17
aeolian deposits, 22-23
beach ridges, 22
colluvial deposits, 23
iron pisoliths, 23, 24
marine terraces and, 17-19
sea cliff erosion and, 25-27
soils and, 23-24
tidepools, 24, 25
uplift/fault activity and, 20-22
Quercus dumosa, 94, 98, 102, 135, 142

R
Rabbits, 114, 129, 136
Raccoon (*Procyon lotor*), 116, 136
Rains. *See* Winter weather
Raptors, 116-117, 118
Rattlesnakes, 123-124, 125, 127
Red algal turf, 62, 65, 67, 77
Red diamond rattlesnake (*Crotalus ruber*), 123, 125, 127

Red racer (*Masticophis flagellum*), 125, 127
Red sea urchin (*Strongylocentrotus franciscanus*), 60, 65, 72, 79
Red-tailed hawk (*Buteo jamaicensis*), 117
Reproductive failure, 77, 78-79, 105, 118
Reptiles, 120-124, 125, 127-128, 130-131, 136
Restoration. *See* Conservation
Rhinocheilus lecontei, 125, 127
Rhus integrifolia, 87, 88, 94, 97, 142
Ring-necked snake, 125
Riprap fill, 27, 75-76
Roadrunner (*Geococcyx californianus*), 129, 139
Rock crab (*Cancer spp.*), 60
Rockweed (*Silvetia fastigiata*), 62, 67, 68, 69
Rocky intertidal habitat, 44, 45, 49, 134-135
adaptive processes in, 67-70
climatic effects and, 72-73
disturbances of, 65-66
ecological threats to, 75-77
kelps in, 64-65, 72, 74
lower intertidal zone, 64-65, 68-69
middle intertidal zone, 62
nursery function of, 72
splash zone, 61, 73
upper intertidal zone, 61-62
zonation and, 61-66
See also Marine systems; Tidepools
Rose-breasted grosbeak (*Pheucticus ludovicianus*), 116
Rose Canyon fault system, 16-17, 21
Rosecrans, William Starke, 150

S
Sagebrush, 88, 89, 92, 94, 95, 96
Saltgrass (*Distichlis spicata*), 94, 99
Salvia mellifera, 88, 94, 96
San Clemente Island, 134
Sandcastle worm (*Phragmatopoma californica*), 68

Sand dunes, 22-23
beach ridges and, 22, 26
foredune scrub and, 98-99, 100
See also Sea cliffs
Sand flows. *See* Cretaceous period; Wave action
San Diego. *See* City of San Diego
San Diego alligator lizard (*Elgaria multicarinata*), 121, 130
San Diego barrel cactus (*Ferocactus viridescens*), 97, 102
San Diego Bay, 21, 54, 56, 78, 112, 135, 142, 145, 149, 154, 155
San Diego gopher snake (*Pituophis catenifer*), 124, 125
San Diego River, 22, 112, 114, 149, 152
San Diego sunflower (*Viguiera laciniata*), 102
Sand Verbena (*Abronia maritima*), 94, 99
Santiago Peak Volcanics rock, 16
Sceloporus occidentalis, 122, 125
Scripps Institution of Oceanography, 47, 81, 168
Scrub oak (*Quercus dumosa*), 94, 98, 102, 135, 142
Sea blight (*Suaeda californica*), 94, 99
Sea caves, 26-27
Sea cliffs, 17-18
aeolian deposits and, 22-23
coastal bluff scrub and, 98, 99, 100
colluvial deposits and, 23
erosive forces and, 25-27
fault scarps, 16
riprap deposits and, 27, 75-76
sea cave collapse process, 26-27
sea stacks and, 27
wave action and, 49
See also Sand dunes
Sea dahlia (*Coreopsis maritima*), 101, 102
Sea grass beds, 67
Sea hare (*Aplysia californica*), 69
Sea level variations, 18-19, 45
Antarctic ice sheet and, 46
intertidal habitat and, 45

rate of rise, 45-46
spring-neap cycle, 47-48
storm surges and, 48-49
tidal ranges, 46-48
uplift activity and, 20
Sea lion, 136
Seals, 136
Sea otter (*Enhydra lutris*), 79, 136, 146-147, 155
Sea stacks, 27
Sea stars, 9, 72, 76
Sea urchin (*Strongylocentrotus spp.*), 60, 65, 66, 72, 74, 77, 79, 81, 147, 154-155
Seaweed. *See* Algae; Kelp forest; Kelps
Sedimentation patterns:
organic sediment, 15
riprap deposit and, 75-76
See also Cretaceous period
Semicossyphus pulcher, 60, 79, 136.155
Serra, Father Junípero, 140, 143
Sewage pollution, 77-78, 81, 154-155
Shaw's agave (*Agave shawii*), 101, 102, 115
Sheephead (*Semicossyphus pulcher*), 60, 79, 136, 155
Short-lobed broomrape (*Orobanche parishii ssp. brachyloba*), 102
Shoulderband snail (*Helmenthoglipta spp.*), 120
Side-blotched lizard (*Uta stansburiana*), 122-123, 125
Silk-spinning cricket (*Cnemotettix miniatus*), 119
Silvery legless lizard (*Aniella pulchra*), 125, 165
Single-bladed kelp (*Laminaria farlowii*), 65, 71
Sivetia fastigiata, 62, 67, 68, 69
Skunk. *See* Striped skunk
Small-flowered microseris (*Microseris douglasii ssp. platycarpha*), 102
Snails, 62, 69, 77, 120, 134
Snake cholla, 102
Snakes, 123-124, 125, 127-128, 130
Soft chaparral species, 86, 91, 95
Soils, 23-24
colluvial deposits, 23

iron pisoliths, 23, 24
management of, 173-174
types of, 24
windblown dust and, 22-23
Solanum xanti, 88
Solitary coral (*Balanophyllia elegans*), 19
Song sparrow (*Zonotrichia melodia*), 118
Southern alligator lizard, 125
Southern California Bight, 34-35, 51, 52
Southern coastal bluff scrub, 98, 99, 100
Southern foredune scrub, 98-99, 100
Southern maritime chaparral, 9, 94, 95, 98, 100
Southern sea palm (*Eisenia arborea*), 64-65
Sow bug (*Porcellio laevis*), 125
Spanish Bight, 152-153
Spanish rule, 142-143, 148
Spea hammondii, 120
Species decline. *See* Ecological threats
Species saturation, 105
Spice bush (*Cneoridium dumosum*), 89
Spiders, 119, 165
Spiny lobster (*Panulirus interruptus*), 60, 78, 79, 155
Spiny-tailed iguana, 125
Stenopelmatus spp., 120
Stink beetle (*Eleodes*), 119
Storm front movement, 38-40
Storm surges, 48-49
Striped racer (*Masticophis lateralis*), 124, 125
Striped skunk (*Mephitis mephitis*), 116
Strongylocentrotus franciscanus, 60
Strongylocentrotus purpuratus, 72, 79
Strongylocentrotus spp., 60, 65, 66, 72, 74, 77, 79, 81, 147, 154-155
Suaeda californica, 94, 99
Summer weather, 33
Catalina Eddy and, 34-35
June gloom, stratus season and, 34, 35
wind patterns, 33-34, 35
See also Climatic conditions; Oceanography;

Winter weather
Sunflower, 102
Sunset Cliffs, 15, 25, 26
Surfgrass (*Phyllospadix torreyi*),
64, 72

T
Taxidea taxus, 114, 129, 136
Terraces. Marine terraces
Tidal action, 46-48
Tidepools, 9, 24, 25, 57, 61
adaptive processes and, 67-68
formation process of, 57-58
kelps in, 64-65, 72
keyed illustration of, 62-63
protection of, 81
syncline features and, 16
tidal action and, 46, 48, 52
trace fossils and, 15
visitation pressures on, 155-
156
wave action and, 49
weed eradication and, 108-
109
Topographic features, 19, 22
Torrey pines, 93
Toxicodendron diversilobum, 89
Toyon tree (*Heteromeles arbutifolia*), 87, 88, 94, 98, 142
Trap door spider (*Aptostichus*),
119, 165
Troglodyte chiton (*Nuttalina
fluxa*), 62
Turban snail, 134, 136
Turf mats, 62, 65, 67

U
Unicorn snail (*Mexicanthina
lugubris*), 69
Uplift activity, 17, 20-22, 26
Uranium dating, 19
Urbanization, 10, 98, 99, 101,
102, 106, 112, 124, 152
Urocyon cineroargenteus, 9, 114,
115
U.S. Coast Guard, 9, 11, 57,
151, 171
U.S. Fish and Wildlife Service
(USFWS), 156, 165, 168-170
U.S. Geological Survey, 10
U.S. Navy, 9, 11, 54, 57, 75, 115,
165, 168, 170, 171
Uta stansburiana, 122-123, 125

V
Vancouver, George, 140
Vermivora celata, 118
Viguiera laciniata, 102
Visitor traffic, 77, 155-156,
166-167
Vizcaíno, Sebastián, 54, 139,
142
Vulpes macrotis macrotis, 114,
128-129, 136

W
Warblers, 116, 118
War. *See* Military activity
Wart-stemmed ceanothus
(*Ceanothus verrucosus*), 88, 94,
98, 102, 103
Water temperatures:
kelp growth and, 74
nutrient levels and, 71-72
See also Climatic conditions
Wave action, 25, 26-27, 49
approach angles, 43, 52
El Niño and, 42-43, 73
fetch, swell and, 49-50
island sheltering effects and,
52
kelp forests and, 71, 73
longshore currents and, 49
northern hemisphere swells,
50
rocky intertidal zone and, 68
southern hemisphere swells,
51
summer winds and, 51
tropical hurricanes and, 50-51
wave sources, 50-51
wind data and, 51
Weather. *See* Climatic conditions
Weed invasion, 107-109, 143
Western fence lizard (*Sceloporus
occidentalis*), 122, 125
Western long-nosed snake
(*Rhinocheilus lecontei*), 125,
127
Western skink, 125
Western spadefoot toad (*Spea
hammondii*), 120
Western toad (*Bufo loreas*), 120
Western yellow-bellied racer
(*Coluber constrictor*), 125, 127
Whale migration, 57, 80
Whelks, 72
White abalone (*Haliotis sorense-
ni*), 79, 148

Wind patterns:
aeolian deposits, 22-23
Catalina Eddy, 34-35
climatic conditions and, 33
Santa Anas, 37-38
summer winds, 33-34, 35, 51
tropical hurricanes, 50-51
winter winds, 37-38
See also Wave action
Winter weather, 35-36
Aleutian low/Great Basin
high pressures and, 36-38
El Niño/La Niña, 41-43, 44
Pacific decadal oscillation
and, 43-44
Santa Ana winds, 37-38
storm front movement,
38-40
variability in, 40-41
See also Climatic conditions;
Oceanography; Summer
weather
Woodrat (*Neotoma*), 115
Worms, 68, 119, 120

X
Xylococcus bicolor, 88, 94, 98

Y
Youth Conservation Corps
(YCC) program, 171-172

Z
Zarhipis spp., 119
Zonation, 61
adaptive processes and, 70
disturbances in, 65-66
evolutionary/adaptive pressures and, 66
fluctuations of, 66
kelp forest and, 65
lower intertidal zone, 64-65,
68-69
middle intertidal zone, 62
plant community groupings,
91-93
splash zone, 61, 73
upper intertidal zone, 61-62
Zonotrichia melodia, 118
Zooplankton, 69
Zúñiga jetty, 150-151, 155

PHOTOGRAPHY AND ILLUSTRATION CREDITS

COVER AND PAGE 8: © Ronald Ray Reekers

FRONTISPIECE: historic map of Point Loma courtesy Cabrillo National Monument, National Park Service

PAGE 5: Map by Deborah Reade

CHAPTER ONE: Patrick Abbott, p. 14, 15, 23, 25, 26, 27; James Blank p. 24; Bill Griswold, p. 13, 18; Deborah Reade, p. 14, 17, 20, 21; San Diego Historical Society, p. 25, 26, 27.

CHAPTER TWO: Cabrillo National Monument, NPS, p. 31, 34, 35; Reinhard E. Flick, p. 44; Bill Griswold, p. 45; Deborah Reade, p. 32, 33, 37, 47, 50; San Diego Historical Society, p. 39; Scripps Institution of Oceanography, p. 43, 52.

CHAPTER THREE: Bonnie J. Becker, p. 66 *right*, 75; Cabrillo National Monument, NPS, p. 76; John Dawson, p. 80; Bill Griswold, p. 66 center, 67 *left*, 68; Eric Hanauer, p. 55, 60, 65 *left*, 67 *right*, 70, 71, 73, 74, 78 *top*; Ron McPeak, ISP Alginates, p. 59, 78 *bottom*; Callie Mack, p. 62-63, 64; Deborah Reade, p. 56, 58.

CHAPTER FOUR: Cabrillo National Monument, NPS, p. 92, 93; Bill Griswold, p. 85, 90, 95, 96-97, 99, 101 *top*, 107; George H. H. Huey, p. 101 *bottom*; Katheryn McEachern, p. 91; Volunteer, p. 86, 87, 89.

CHAPTER FIVE: Chris Brown, p. 113, 115, 116, 117, 119, 120, 121, 122, 123, 124, 127; Don Kohlbaur, p. 114.

CHAPTER SIX: Cabrillo National Monument, NPS, p. 147, 149 bottom, 153; City of San Diego, Wastewater Dept., p. 155; Bill Griswold, p. 154; Susan Leach, courtesy Grand Canyon Association, p. 134; San Diego Historical Society, p. 133, 137, 142, 143, 145 *bottom*, 149 *top*, 150; San Francisco Maritime Museum Association, p. 146; Richard Schlect, courtesy NPS, Harpers Ferry Center, p. 140-141; J. Wegter, courtesy Fort Guijarros Museum Foundation, p. 145 top.

CHAPTER SEVEN: Cabrillo National Monument, NPS, p. 167, 172; Gary Davis, p. 165; J. P. Harris, p. 163 *bottom*; U.S. Navy, p. 169; San Diego Historical Society, p. 160; San Diego State University, p. 162; Mary Wick, courtesy Point Loma Native Plant Preserve, p. 170; Samantha Weber, p. 159, 163 *bottom*.

ABOUT THE PAPER

This book is printed on New Leaf Reincarnation Matte paper, 100% recycled, 50% post-consumer waste, and processed chlorine free. We've chosen to use this paper to reinforce our belief in the importance of environmental responsibility and to inspire others to help conserve the earth's precious resources. Even small conservation efforts go a long way towards the larger goal of environmental preservation.